CINDERELLA AND THE
THREE WISE MEN

CINDERELLA AND THE THREE WISE MEN

Or How To Be A Vicar's Wife Without Really Crying

CELIA ANDREWS

CHERRY TREE HOUSE BOOKS

First published in 2004 by:
Cherry Tree House Books
Cherry Tree House
Ham Lane
Kingston Seymour
North Somerset
BS21 6XE

Reprinted in May 2005

ISBN: 0 9549211 0 0

Printed and bound in Great Britain by:
ProPrint, Riverside Cottages, Old Great North Road, Stibbington,
Cambridgeshire PE8 6LR

CONTENTS

PREFACE

Someone who, in these politically correct days, had better not be named once said they thought I had a 'vocation to be a Vicar's wife'. That conjured up visions of me lurking outside a theological college waiting to pounce on a likely ordinand. In the event what happened was I married a journalist who turned into a Vicar and I continued my own career as a journalist, fitting in parish matters around the job and children.

The narrator here, therefore, is only a rough approximation of myself – I am closer to another character in the saga – and in any case these days we are referred to as 'spouses' because the incumbent is very likely to be a woman. The people you meet in these pages are likewise rough approximations and almalgams of those I have met over many years and the aim is not to give portraits of individuals but a feel of the experience of living in a vicarage – with or without a vocation for it.

DEDICATION

For John, Jane and Matthew,
My inspiration and fellow inhabitants of
The Vicarage

CHAPTER ONE

PANTOMANIA

January 1 Thursday

Solved problem of pantomime giant's head – found one in our loft. Goodness knows how long it's been there gathering cobwebs round its whiskers – or which incumbent used it for what. Tried it on giant, Jimmy Kealing – complained it smells. It does, so sprinkled it with talc and threatened to give giant's part to his brother, so that's alright. Putting on panto and Nativity Play with same cast a mistake. Next year must write Cinderella And The Three Wise Men and it can do as both.

Carli's mother threatening to take her to see gran on day of show. I'd better prepare to play heroine as well as props, third villager, bailiff and tea lady. Dame and Jack broke six of best hall cups in kitchen scene. My fault – should have brought some of our grotty ones.

January 2 Friday

Carli went to gran today so just missed final rehearsal. Only words she knows are 'Why, here's Jack. What are you doing this fine day?' and says them every time she comes on. Jason Fearns and Christopher Bowles fight real duels with plastic swords and keep breaking them.

Stanley rang to say hall's inside toilet blocked. Outside toilet full of leaves and spare chairs and cistern cracked by tramp who spent the night there. Didn't inform Stanley that as churchwarden it was his responsibility, so I'll have to do something.

January 3 Saturday

Don't ask how it went, diary. Just don't ask. Beanstalk fell over and covered most of stage – everyone had to climb across it. Christopher swore when he fell over it. Bought the shop's last plastic sword which broke at first hostilities (off stage) so had to make cardboard ones. Giant killed too soon. No way of clearing loo so took our porta potty for inside toilet.

Three kids asked if we could do a panto next year. Must start work on Dick Whittington Meets The Shepherds Abiding In The Fields.

January 4 Sunday

Attendance at Church low after glut of carol services, Christingles etc. Miss Cavendish said the giant's head was used at fetes for having balls thrown in the mouth at 3d a go. If it's that old, no wonder it smelled.

January 5 Monday

New Year Resolution – sort out hall bookings. Colin given scruffy notes, forgets them, endless panic over double bookings. Three lots booked for Twelfth Night parties tomorrow. Folk dance group and Derby and Joan agreed to share hall. Brownies coming here for disco.

Leonard, hall caretaker, rang in full spate: 'Some ****
left a ***ing potty and it's *** well flooded the ****y hall. If it's not ****ing emptied in half a ****ing hour you can take your **** hall and . . .' (but I'm not writing that even with a blank. Doesn't he know any normal adjectives?) 'You'll need to see to it for this damn do tonight. Looks like snow and that hall's a bugger for burst pipes.'

January 6 Tuesday

Brown Owl rang to say 36 coming to disco. Anne and John disgusted at their home taken over – again. Disco outfit arrived with DJ and flashing lights. Put food in sitting room, tied up cupboard doors against earth tremors. 49 kids came and jigged about. Anne and John joined in – their age group more or less.

January 7 Wednesday

Brown Owl's helpers collected equipment, dead sandwiches, cans and three abandoned pairs of shoes. Two Brownies handed me return slips for Sunday School outing to proper panto Saturday. Saturday! Last thought of it before Christmas.

Dredged up other slips from leaking glue, broken crayons, mangled Nativity Play scripts in Sunday School bag. 45 of us going but only 43 tickets. Also found Jason Fearn's water pistol confiscated during Nativity Play rehearsals as unlikely gift from Wise Men. Now ashamed of myself. Christ child would have laughed. Must include it in next year's script.

Children back at school. I forgot – mad scramble for clean clothes and packed lunches.

January 8 Thursday

Let kitchen boiler go out, for good. Costs too much, fed up clearing ashes like a Victorian skivvy.

January 9 Friday

Resolved to do more visiting, starting with Mrs Daniels of big house along Back Lane. Arthur mentioned her Sunday. He could go but churchwarden not the same as the Vicarage Family (think he's afraid of her from when her family were village Top People). She doesn't go out much. Kids say house is haunted – rubbish, but I called in daylight, just in case.

Very scary. Mrs Daniels, over coffee in bone china, said 'What shall I do about Cedric?' Cedric, as in household ghost, died 1763 not romantically but in bed of ague at 87. Now plays organ in the cellar at night – loudly and wrongly. Aggravates the dog. Little I know of counselling did not cover any of that. Muttered something about exorcism and left.

January 10 Saturday

All turned up for outing to panto. Not enough seats so Lisa Turner – bandbox child with never a hair out of place – sat on my lap. I got chocolate on her pink dress and also caught it in loo door in interval. Serves me right – should ethically have paid for two extra seats.

Six of kids got on wrong coach going home and were brought back just as I had rung police about abduction. Rang and cancelled.

Was going to remind everyone of Sunday School starting tomorrow – seemed mean so I didn't. Also too busy avoiding Lisa's mother.

School Essay: How I Spent My Christmas Holidays By Carli Sims

I was in a pantomime, Jack and the Beanstalk, as a princess. Why here's Jack. What are you doing this fine day I said. There was more words but to much. Miss was cross I didn't know any but more cross with Christopher for saying bad word when he felled over and with some boys for braking the cups and sords. I went to a big pantomime with the Sunday School but not to Sunday School. Mummy said there was to much church at Christmas. I like colering and singing. Misses class for the big one is borring I think.
Our brownies had a disco at her house and brown owl said it was better than nothing and not to drop food or make a mess, but sum did.

January 11 Sunday

Sunday School. Only had three glue sticks stuck together, empty felt tips, gumless sticky paper, broken scissors and used play dough. After years of making papier maché Green Hills Far Away, clay praying hands, puppet scenes and Parable Of The Sower with real cress the kids get to the top class and me telling unillustrated stories and making up prayers. They take it in good part.

January 12 Monday

Snowed. Children home from school. We put up a family of five for the night. Write about it later – must save two halves of candles I found when power went off. No hot water in tank as I've stopped using the boiler and the immersion's electric. Others not pleased.

January 13 Tuesday

Colin found candle ends in Church. Six people came to cook food in our gas stove – embarrassing as haven't cleaned it from Christmas. Visitors left at lunch time – couple whose car broke down at our gate – two boys and baby crying so asked them in. Kept saying they were 'not Church goers, I'm afraid' as though it was a disease they hadn't had and didn't want to catch.

January 14 Wednesday

Electricity back on. Stanley rang to say did I know hall kitchen flooded. Kitchen? I said – a change from the loo. He'd mended whatever it was but water everywhere. Did I know six of the best cups were missing? Went and bailed out kitchen – never seen drawers full of water before.

January 15 Thursday

Worried about Mrs Daniels – cold old house and ghost stories would scare off possible helpers. Went round and found two sets of footprints – one to end of garden, one back to house. She seemed cheerier. 'Snow?' she said when asked if she was alright. 'I hadn't noticed. Cedric has found peace. And it's all thanks to you dear.' Finally, a talent to make up for not sewing, flower arranging, gardening or cleaning. Ghost laying. She'd waited till the dog's howling signalled Cedric was there, opened all doors (in the snow!) walked to the 'nice peaceful copse', dug a grave, said the funeral service, filled in the grave and walked back. No howling dog, no sudden coldness, no organ playing. 'I'm glad for him,' she said 'But it's lonely here now.' Got a few fires going, found her a few candles.

January 16 Friday

Most of snow gone but called off choir practice. Nice to have evening at home with children.

January 17 Saturday

Rural Dean's 'party' – the dreaded Johnson there. Tried to forget stories about him and skip full of whisky bottles, forgetting funerals and weddings, ringing a bell for wife to get him things.

(Grace Johnson not at do, probably didn't tell her it was on). Did he really give those (possibly human) bones to his awful mangy dog when he illegally dug up flagstones in his Church?

Geoffrey, new Rural Dean, looked bemused as Johnson got noisier and drunker. Suspect deanery clergy only voted Geoffrey RD because he never notices what's going on and wouldn't have know about Johnson. Colin and I took Johnson home and decanted him in his porch, rang doorbell and fled. Poor Grace.

January 18 Sunday

Snow all gone. Forgot the birds again. Vicarages ought to be a refuge for distressed birds but keep forgetting to put out crumbs.

Church organ's notes stuck. Unaccompanied version of drearier hymns rather good.

January 19 Monday

Colin forgot to announce St John Ambulance jumble sale and ask for volunteers and cakes. Must ask Jumble Queen, Mrs Padget, get my kids to volunteer to help and start baking. Jumble will turn up on its own.

January 20 Tuesday

In drive this morning – six bags of coal, four of kindling wood, three old doors, ten musty sacks. Ancient estate car rolled up with planks, corrugated iron sheeting, two dustbins.

Donald Brown's moving day. I forgot he promised the Church 'some bits and pieces to sell for Funds'. Never comes to Church but feels someone should keep it standing up in case he ever needs to. Meant to tell Colin as he's trained to turn down offers without offence, but forgot. Too late for refusal. Thanked him, wished him well.

Leaned doors, wood, corrugated iron against garage wall. Colin not that cross – thinks he could make a bicycle shed. Meanwhile stowed it all somewhere.

January 21 Wednesday

Arthur, who knows everything through owning small factory and living here all his life, says Donald Brown sold house to a single woman in her late 40s. And someone saw piles of men's clothes being unpacked from her removal van.

Arthur thinks I should visit because she's 'Church'; Colin thinks I should go round because she's a newcomer; nosy neighbours because of finding out about the Mystery Man; me because she might be useful. Better let them settle in and find the teapot first. People put not offering Vicar's wife cups of tea high upon their list of cardinal sins.

Still baking for Jumble.

January 22 Thursday

It's only her brother – an eccentric allergic to clergy and Church, collects dead motor bikes. His sister, Joyce Neale, said she's willing to join the choir as an alto but it's a bit of a come down and she's shocked to hear we're not affiliated to the Royal School of Church Music. (Bet they wouldn't let our organist Derek set Victorian hymns to television jingles). Didn't tell Joyce about Derek. She starts tomorrow at choir practice. She's been a tutor at a sixth form college for years. You can tell.

January 23 Friday

Choir practices are certainly going to liven up in future. Joyce got her own way over everything from hymn tunes to how to process neatly.

Still baking gingerbread, queen cakes and biscuits. That should be enough.

Letter From Joyce Neal To Her Friend Hazel

Dear Hazel
Simon and I duly removed our goods and chattels last week – not to mention his dreadful engines – and are firmly ensconced in our new home. You must pay us a visit when professional duties allow. I am sure you will be intrigued by the little community in which we find ourselves.

I know I was adamant about not getting involved, but the Vicar's wife was so prompt in visiting and so insistent on the need for a trained alto voice and experienced musical presence that I felt unable to refuse her invitation to join the Church choir. She is sadly scatterbrained I feel and rushed off saying something about a Jumble Sale. Really. I thought that stereotyped Vicar's wife only existed in amateur theatricals.

The choir is in desperate need of a firm hand, I discovered at the first practice. However, when I recall how your dear brother, you and I created our magnificent madrigal group out of most unpromising material, I do not despair of achieving something here. The organist, Derek something, will be the main thorn in the flesh it seems, being the exact antithesis of your dear brother at St Saviour's. This Derek's repertoire of voluntaries seems to be confined to light secular music and he has not that 'feel' for liturgy so essential to Church organists. However, h e seems the type of person likely to be amenable to suggestion.

I enclose the photographs of our holiday . . .

January 24 Saturday

Got up at 7am, made more small cakes. (If I get on the right side of the St John's people they might give a demonstration at our fete). John backed out of helping because of pressing business with two friends and a computer game. Anne agreed to help. Cakes solid − forgot to take them out of freezer. Anne and I on women's clothes − jettisoned old corsets. Three o'clock four women arrived to set out hall for child's birthday party. Sold them T shirts and condiment set with missing mustard pot, gave them free cups of tea while trying to decide what to do. Certain I never had a call about Jimmy Kealing's birthday party − I'd have hidden the rest of the good cups if I'd know. Mrs Padget cut everything to half price, did a roaring trade. Customers hustled out at 3.30, tables cleared by 3.45, party set up by 4. Stored jumble in attic after seven wheelbarrow trips through the garden. Colin very evasive about double booking of hall.

Leonard made a ****y fuss about cleaning mixture of jelly and old shoes, balloons and second hand underwear from hall. It's his job and he didn't see the half of it.

CHAPTER TWO

STOP PRESS

January 25 Sunday

Joyce so at home you'd think she'd been here ten years. Certain straightening of backs when she arrives, plus dropping of rogue dotted crochets and sounding of S and T at end of words. Reminds me of a Latin teacher at school and everyone else of their former teachers, including Colin. Derek struck up with something from The Sound of Music as a recessional. I looked at Joyce – tiny smile flickered. She also comes to Evensong. Psalm singing needs attention.

Disaster at home. Ben's broken his leg. I don't hold out much hope as a gerbil's so tiny. Anne's devastated.

January 26 Monday

Vet put gerbil's leg in matchstick splint. Ben ate it. Vet put leg in plaster. Ben ate it. Vet's advice – let him heal himself.

January 27 Tuesday

Ben drags his leg carefully behind him and seems to have prescribed himself bed rest between meals.

January 28 Wednesday

Magazine typing day. Not much material. Tempted to put in dreadful slushy poem Mrs Padget sent last year which I told her I'd 'mislaid'. No sign of Colin's Vicar's letter. Or the calendar. Or sidesmen's rota. Or Women's Hour, of course. They keep their meetings so secret, even from Colin, I dread to think what they do – knit shrouds for garden gnomes? Brew pink gin? Cast spells?

January 29 Thursday

Typed out magazine stuff twice as computer crashed and I'd not saved it. So short of stuff launched Mothers and Toddlers Group Colin keeps trying to get round to, printed the poem and wrote

9

Colin's letter for him – stirring stuff. Extra careful with spelling, grammar etc. because of Joyce.

January 30 Friday

Cleared up after herd of Sam Thompson's cows stampeded through garden in the early hours.

Young mum arrived with baby. Gave her tea. She lives in Johnson's parish, wants the baby baptised with us because she was married in our Church. Colin said he would but must contact Johnson for permission. Look of alarm flickered across her face.

January 31 Saturday

Sam Thompson brought round bottle of whisky as the nearest he'll get to apologising for his cows. He said few gardens could have noticed the damage as little as ours. Later Colin said he was glad I didn't make any sarcastic comments as he's buttering Sam up because farm implements are useful for shifting tables and chairs etc for parish events. I doubt he'll succeed with a man who puts tacks in his drive to discourage callers and threw his daughter's boyfriend in a pond because he thought a Jersey was a sort of sweater. Or so I heard.

Colin still hasn't rung Johnson about that Baptism.

February 1 Sunday

Choir sounding altogether more professional these days. Even old favourite hymns have acquired new lease of life. Derek's beginning to play voluntaries out of a proper book and that makes processing in and out much easier for those of us not good at dance steps.

February 2 Monday

Colin took day off and went berserk with our cash – bought us pub lunch, himself two non clerical shirts and an antique desk to replace scruffy table he'd been using. Desk too beautiful for computer to sit on so he's still got the table. Give it three weeks before desk invisible under junk. Better drop my Campaign For More Days Off before he bankrupts us.

February 3 Tuesday

Colin asked Johnson about Baptism. Johnson regards mother and family as troublemakers – reason unspecified – doesn't agree to Colin doing ceremony. Says would Colin be 'kind enough to leave him to deal with is own parishioners.'

February 4 Wednesday

Hunted out Anne and John's old toys for Mothers and Toddlers Group. Young mum (Brenda) and baby from Johnson's parish arrived. Over tea confessed full facts of family dealing with Johnson. He turned up drunk at her sister's wedding and her father threatened him with a churchwarden's staff he grabbed from pew. Brenda fiddled the residential qualifications so she could marry her Pete in our Church before we came – now worried at what a drunken Johnson could do holding small baby over font full of water, even holy water. Johnson's refused to do it anyway. I couldn't think of an answer to her problem. Baby slept throughout visit. Colin can't think what to do either.

February 5 Thursday

Leonard heard lots of messy kids to be let loose in his precious hall. Said he's not paid to clear up after etc. etc. Actually he is, and quite well, but I promised to put down a bit of carpet, wash up crockery, keep sticky fingers from the piano and clear up without using his personal supply of cleaning materials and utensils.

Miss Cavendish rang in a terrible state. Her landlord, Sam Thompson, is to pull down her cottage as he says it's an eyesore, and doesn't see why he should house her just because her late father worked on his farm ages ago. I went round. Found her expecting miracles from Colin.

February 6 Friday

I thought, if choir's getting a new image perhaps we could throw our female headgear – three cornered cap guaranteed to flatten hairdos and fall off if you're straining to reach top notes. No good asking Joyce to do something as her hair is always in a severe bun not even a ton weight could flatten – and as an alto she doesn't have top notes. Invited them all to a 'do' at ours later this month to soften them up – didn't say what I was plotting.

February 7 Saturday

Tame local reporter, Stephanie Bartram, wanted to see Colin – I stayed in the room. Brenda's father told The Echo her story – Warring Vicars Spurn Baby Gerald (at least I know its name and sex now, I thought) (no I don't. Stephanie thinks the newspaper might have got it wrong).

Felt sorry for Stephanie as she's got a crush on Colin, never gets the story her paper wants, is a faithful soul and slamming Vicars upsets her, travels everywhere on an awful moped that breaks down and leaves her pushing it and turning up at events in a helmet. She mournfully took notes as Colin kept saying he had to obey the rules. She tramped off to see Johnson, leaving broken down moped in our drive.

February 8 Sunday

Miss Cavendish cornered Colin about her housing problem. He seems to think he's so friendly with Sam these days he'll be able to fix it.

Most of choir coming to supper on 27th. Most realise I'm up to something.

February 9 Monday

Poor old Canon Perry had a stroke last night – not expected to live. Pretty doddery, but did mind the shop on our holidays. Once preached 20 minutes about the Bible but substituted the word 'Bicycle' throughout. Colin with him and his wife most of day.

If you live long enough in a Vicarage you hear everything, I suppose. The phone went mid morning and it was Mrs Delaware from the Big House (Family been there since village was mud huts and hunter gatherers though now fallen on what passes for hard times with them). Wanted to speak to Colin. 'He's out, I'm afraid,' I said, trying not to put on a Mrs Bucket accent, but failing I'm afraid. 'Can I help?' 'So sorry,' she said,

'I'm afraid it's a matter for squire and parson.' Honestly she did, diary.

Colin went round. Mrs Delaware's heard of Miss Cavendish's problem and wants to offer her a run down cottage on her estate as her duty to the village. 'But it's unfit for human habitation,' I said in my normal accent this time. 'She means well. You shouldn't take that attitude,' he said. He passed on the offer to Miss Cavendish. Her reaction? Much the same as mine.

February 10 Tuesday

PCC meeting. Colin reported on scheme to replace plain window with stained glass commemorating some guy from village who founded minor missionary society last century. Ellery I think his name was. Village newcomers want him remembered.
The-seven-generations-in-the-village-and-another-one on-the-way people don't want it as Ellery never came back or showed any interest in us and several other people are more worthy of stained glass. Also very expensive.

Canon Perry no better. Colin got in late from meeting. Stanley had taken him for a drink afterwards – always a worrying sign.

February 11 Wednesday

Canon Perry died in the night. Everyone will miss him, dear old soul. Colin cut up about it. Told me the cost of stained glass so high the Ellery Fan Club wants to ask the family to help pay. What family?

Colin saw Sam, who said surely the 'old girl' (Miss Cavendish) qualified for a council flat. Several in village want to go to newspaper about it. Wonderful, I said. The same paper would have a piece about Colin not helping an elderly parishioner and not baptising a baby. Stephanie then arrived to do a piece on Parish Feud Over Memorial Window.

Colin's beginning to look his age.

Extract from Stephanie Bartram's Diary

Dear diary, what shall I do? I'm torn between my duty to the paper and my duty to The Church – or, to tell the truth to you alone, my duty to dear C....

The editor revels in stories that crucify The Church and takes pleasure in forcing me to cover them. Subs slash my reports to ribbons and twist my words out of all recognition.

C... is too upright to realise how cruelly he will be misrepresented and the very thought of causing him pain is torture to me. And through all this I have to keep my love a deadly secret, although I sometimes fear – or is it hope? – that glances passing between C.... and me at choir practice (never in a service) mean that he Understands. SHE is very pleasant with her cups of coffee but incapable of appreciating his fine and unworldly nature.

Ah well, perhaps if I avoid the sensational in my style and write the Baptism and the old lady's house and window row as separate stories and hand them in when the editor is out – drinking as usual – they will be buried at the back of the paper. Most of my stories are.

February 12 Thursday

We gained a cabbage, but the tax people mustn't know. Colin had a funeral in Church (old man Colin didn't know until called to his death bed) and someone whispered to him at the graveside 'check the table at the back of the Church, Vicar.' There he found a rather grand cabbage. It felt very Victorian to be paid in kind – and illicit too as we are supposed to declare all gifts to the tax man.

Problem finding the man a burial spot after row with Mr Mason last year. He keeps unofficial record of where everyone is buried and where they want to be buried if it's a family grave. Took offence over Colin's 'Romish Practices', now refuses to let anyone see the records. New undertakers had trouble finding empty spot. Half expected to see Stephanie round again – They Dug Up Aunty headline – but mercifully she seems to have gone back to WI and coffee morning reports.

I hope Canon Perry's family agree to cremation.

February 13 Friday

Diocesan Communications Officer, Canon Hopkins – tall, gaunt, unmarried, short fuse – rang about the three stories in The Echo about us: non Baptised baby, non stained glass window, non pastoral care of old lady in housing struggle. I quipped that they'd not heard the one about the graveyard muddle yet and I could hear him suppressing worse language even that Leonard would use. He said we must refer all media calls to him. Colin snatched the phone and toadied to him and heard the national newspapers are working on Heartless Vicar Must Go, Say Parishioners.

Stanley rang to say he was about to go to his daughter's for a few days. Coward. Arthur came round to say, after 20 minutes dithering, that he supported Colin *Whatever happened.*

Miss Cavendish called in tears at having landed Colin in it. Sat her down with tea and sympathy. Stephanie arrived, also in tears. Her editor thinks she should have done better, national journalists are trying to get her contacts and she's terrified Colin will blame her. Also 'a very rude Canon' told her she had a greater duty to the Church than the paper. Colin heard the crying and rushed off to visit the sick.

At choir practice Joyce said why didn't Colin blackmail Johnson into doing the Baptism by saying he'd do it regardless. Also why didn't we decide on a cheaper memorial to Ellery and get the missionary society to pay. Personally she thought Miss Cavendish wanted to go into a sheltered flat but didn't want to betray her late family by leaving their house. Of course, as a newcomer, she wasn't trying to interfere. I mentioned the graveyard business. She said at school she always gave troublemakers a responsible job.

February 14 Saturday

Colin's birthday. Only a grim smile when given his presents. Calls still coming in from papers – referred all to the Canon. Geoffrey the Rural Dean finally realised what was happening – lovely man but slow on the uptake, two notes behind in all hymns. I said we had plans to solve all problems – didn't credit Joyce with any of it. He said 'good, good.'

National Newspaper Report

Parishioners in the farming village of Lockstone are calling for the resignation of the Vicar they say has failed to help his flock in times of need. Revd Colin Buckfast is said to have:
- *Refused to baptise a baby because of a personal vendetta against the Vicar of a neighbouring parish;*
- *Refused to back an elderly parishioner in her battle with a rich landowner to keep her family home;*
- *Refused to allow a stained glass window to be dedicated to a missionary member of a well know local family;*

Vicar of the neighbouring parish, Revd Laurence Johnson, said: 'I don't know why this man is letting an argument he has with me deny this helpless baby a Christian baptism. I will do everything I can to help in this sad situation.' Revd Buckfast was unavailable for comment but a Church spokesman, Canon Vincent Hopkins, said: 'He has been under a considerable strain lately.'

February 15 Sunday

Everyone at Church thrilled at being in the limelight – only problem, how to prolong it and get on local television. Lower Dalton was filmed last year and all they had was Vicar In Sex Rumpus followed by We're Backing The Vicar, Say Villagers.

Miss Cavendish refused offers of help to barricade herself into her home. She seemed very thoughtful.

February 16 Monday

Canon Perry funeral and (thank goodness) cremation. Church full. Johnson there and Colin told him he was going to do the Baptism. Even Johnson couldn't shout at a clergy funeral. Lay yes. Clergy, no. He stamped off. Mr Mason crept in at back. He was always fond of the Canon so I suppose it's not really significant – but it is a start.

February 17 Tuesday

We made it on television but everyone's furious it was only the bishop outside his palace saying he stood by his clergy. We'd all dressed up in our best being-interviewed gear and gone shopping rather a lot with a wary eye out for cameras. Miss Cavendish is understood to have gone to the council offices, which could mean a tame end to that story line.

CHAPTER THREE

GOOD SHEPHERDS

February 18 Wednesday

Never mind the newspaper stories, the greatest news yet is a just retired cleric has moved into one of the new bungalows. I wanted Colin to go round to carry him over the threshold and sign him up for holiday services in perpetuity. He refused, saying he needed to know more about the retired man first. What's to know except that he's physically and legally able to take Holy Communion services.

February 19 Thursday

He's great, Revd Dennis Bailey. So lovely there has to be a catch – unfrocked or closet happy-clappy man. I don't care. Colin so vague about when he meant to call I went myself. We chatted as though friends for 20 years. His wife, Elsie, volunteered to show me over the bungalow – odd as those bungalows are about as architecturally outstanding as a cardboard box. As we inspected the broom cupboard I realised why the tour. She said could Colin use Dennis for the odd service to get him out from under her feet. Was there any other job he could do around the parish? I told her to consider him hired from today. They're coming to tea tomorrow.

February 20 Friday

Typical of Johnson. After all the fuss he's to Baptise baby Geraldine (finally the right name) himself. Colin still half believes Dennis is a figment of my fevered imagination as he was out on a funeral visit when the Baileys arrived for tea. The bereaved family wants a burial. If Judgement Day doesn't come before the end of next week and cause everyone to rise up and let us see where they are buried, we could have angry scenes and more headlines.

February 21 Saturday

Arthur rang to say did we know a retired vicar had moved into the new bungalows and we'd better call. It's the first time I've ever visited before his nudging.

February 22 Sunday

Miss Cavendish has told Sam she's willing to leave her house and had he thought of doing it up and selling it. She's arranged herself a sheltered flat with a warden in that block just outside our parish boundary.

Baileys in church. Got on well with everyone. Six people suggested Colin should ask Dennis to take a few services – without me having to give hints.

February 23 Monday

The dead can rest easy. Mr Mason's back plotting the graves. Most recent death was a friend of his, had to find where his family was buried. Colin treated him like the Prodigal Son when he came round – I treated him to tea and biscuits (closest we had to fatted calf without slaughtering one of Sam's). Colin asked Mr Mason if he'd like to be appointed official Graveyard Keeper – he was delighted. We've never had one of those before. If you detect the Voice of Joyce in all this, diary, you're right.

Met Stanley while I was out laden with food for choir supper. He said I could do with transport. Still haven't cleaned the cooker so will make the kitchen out of bounds. Downstairs loo only flushes for friends and relatives.

February 24 Tuesday

Stanley arrived with battered bike his married daughter left to rot in shed. Shall I ever dare to ride it after 15 years on foot?

Miss Cavendish really glad about move, proud of talking Sam into saving the house. Joyce behind it all I bet. Colin to borrow Sam's van to move her. I'll help pack.

Operation clear up at our house for Friday – odd bits of food from disco behind sideboard and piano. Wish I was sort of

19

housewife to have cleared up the day after. No I don't. Too boring.

February 25 Wednesday

Helped Miss Cavendish pack. Not a trace of sentimentality over odds and ends. 'I'm quite excited about it, dear,' she said. 'Absolutely nothing has happened to me in my life and now I'm starting something new at 72.'

First session of Mothers and Toddlers in hall. Eight mums, 11 kids, three broken cups, (not best), four fights over the only riding-on toy. Making tea, washing up, clearing up I don't mind. Being treated like a gran, I do. Mums kept asking me how we dealt with nappies, potty training, sitters *in my day*. Forgot to turn off gas fires. Remembered at 2am, tried out new bike in my nightgear through our garden to the hall. I can still cycle!

February 26 Thursday

Began work on magazine – very rushed and messy. First person to complain can take over. Made food for tomorrow. Dusted in dining room. Shut piano lid to hide grubby keys.

February 27 Friday

Choir plus spouses turned up for supper. My cooking always tastes alright, just looks odd. Most know this and tuck in. Got them to agree to scrap female headgear but Mrs Fearns said choir looked smart in them when they sang for her wedding 40 years ago. Derek kept looking morosely at Joyce – thinks she's hoping to introduce more anthems to our repertoire and he's quite happy with All In The April Evening and a couple more. His neat little wife used to try to make him change his ways but since her death no one else has tried.

Joyce said would we like her to contact a friend in the county music library and see if she could borrow some anthems.

Note From Mrs Fearns The Next Morning

Thank you so much for the supper, which was kind of you to think of the choir as most don't but expect us to turn up and sing in all weathers, including those modern hymns for the Sunday School that don't turn up.

PS Not only me thinks you should keep the hats and lots would have said only didn't like to and thought it was no good saying anyway. Things that have been in the Church should be kept and not thrown away like the old services and hymns and it's not right to be so high.

February 28 Saturday

Sam's motive in lending truck is now obvious – wants to use our back 'lawn' (quotation marks his) to graze some sheep. Colin agreed. Also Sam's granddaughter's got a pony that's coming to our paddock. Colin remembered he'd promised Leonard he could keep six ducks in the garden. I asked not to be present when Leonard heard of yet another treble booking – Sam's sheep, his ducks and a horse.

March 1 Sunday

Our newspaper stories eclipsed by two churchwardens – opposite sexes – from the next deanery vanishing from their homes and reappearing suspiciously close to each other up North somewhere. Stanley jokingly said he knew of no lady likely to lure him from parish duties – not even the Vicar's wife.

March 2 Monday

Removal of Miss Cavendish a non event. No angry scenes with wicked landlord, just final wave to house with her umbrella. Colin drove Sam's truck with furniture to her new home. I asked her about the brass bed she and all her family were born in. She said 'I got Fred Padget to bury it in the garden. I couldn't be bothered to put it in a sale.' Personally I think she can't bear to think of anyone else sleeping in it. The new owners are in for a surprise if they decide to put in a swimming pool or a conservatory and start digging.

March 3 Tuesday

Time to stop ignoring the youth club and *do something*. Ex leaders, Sally and Bill Richards, moved months ago. Since then the PCC has taken it in turns to take sessions – those that don't mind turning out after 7pm. I heard Stanley ran a treasure hunt and lost them all.

Joyce said to me politely did we know our youth group had a reputation for running wild through the streets every second Saturday night? I said we were in 'a state of transition' with great plans for the future. Come to think of it, if I'd told her the ghastly truth instead of automatically covering up she might have volunteered to help – that'd serve the little beasts right. Too late now. I shall have to do something myself.

Meant to discuss it with Colin but he was out on a Baptism visit. Came home pleased with himself. Baby's parents run a pub and, while waiting for a break in business to talk to them, he played the fruit machine and won the jackpot.

March 4 Wednesday, Ash Wednesday

Can't give up chocolate for Lent as I don't really like the stuff so will do something about the youth group as a penance. Colin appalled when I told him of Joyce's words – hardly less so when I offered to do something. But, any port in a storm I could see him thinking. Anne and John didn't want to join.

Lent Lunches again. Mrs Fearns in charge again. Raising money for the Third World by doing without a meal. Wish she'd let us do it with French sticks and tinned soup instead of making things like wholemeal quiches and thin gruel apparently made with disused cabbage water.

Mothers and Toddlers still fighting over the one ride-on toy – mothers being more argumentative but the children better at crafty kicks and punches.

March 5 Thursday

Brilliant idea – consulted the Baileys about youth group. Dennis and Elsie said they'd always managed to run a pretty good youth group. One of their ex members was considering the priesthood, one of their drama section plays small parts on TV and one boy is now responsible for many national advertisements thanks to craft work he did at youth group. Colin still reserving judgement on Dennis until after he's taken his first service – Sunday evening.

Sam's workforce came this afternoon to put up fences for his animals.

March 6 Friday

Leonard and his ducks arrived as Sam turned up with sheep in a landrover – ducks seemed glad of the company. Pony arrived and looks very big. Parked the bike to offer it a mint – it nudged over the bike, scattering shopping. Sam said we were welcome to sell the manure for Church funds. I hastily said it seemed an unlikely fundraiser but four people enquired about it for their gardens today. I told them to feel free to help themselves.

Joyce arrived at choir practice with some pleasant but simple Easter anthems. Derek had found two distinctly modern pieces. No question which the choir preferred – conservative is too soft a term for us.

I felt sorry for Derek –not his fault I'd recruited an awful bossy woman. If we're not careful some parish with guitars and tambourines will snaffle him. I told Derek the Sunday School could use his pieces if he'd teach them – he seemed satisfied, for now. I said we'd try a week without choir hats to see what people thought. Mrs Fearns' other protesters not forthcoming – she just snorted.

March 7 Saturday

Hurtled out in car to go to town for shopping and child eye appointments – three sheep and some lambs wandering in drive. Ducks rushing round in state of panic. All seemed happy enough so I drove round flock and out of gate. Saw other ewes and lambs cropping grass verge along road. Ran back to phone Sam. Wife said he was out until 9pm. Sheep wandering along middle of road, much tooted by passers by. Colin put trousers on over pyjamas ('one Saturday of year I have a lie in and etc. etc. etc.') and we chased them about a bit, up and down road. Leonard arrived to feed ducks, slapped ewes on bottoms, sent them flying up the drive and home. He swore. So did Colin. I left them making temporary repairs to the fences, still swearing. I was late for appointments.

March 8 Sunday

Pub baby baptised. Parents still bemused over Colin playing their fruit machine. Dennis Bailey preached at Evensong. Disappointing, I thought. Long and pretty dull. Colin said 'very sound' so Dennis is here to stay. 'Boring, isn't he?' someone said. 'Very sound,' I answered. Lack of choir hats passed unnoticed by congregation.

March 9 Monday

Wonderful. Finally got Colin out for whole day (Church crawling, but I mustn't complain) and this happens. Got home just as children did to find burglar had smashed bay window and taken the video machine, plus instructions from kitchen drawer. Sent Colin to search for intruder – no sign. Police arrived with fingerprint kits, interrogation techniques, clue searching etc. – don't think they'll find him, I'm glad to say. It's a comic adventure unless the burglar has a face. Anne didn't see the comic side. The video had in it her favourite tape.

Phone kept ringing with expressions of curiosity. Leonard came up trumps – measured window, fetched glass, put it in. I don't care what he called the burglar, or the glass when he smashed the first pane and had to get another.

March 10 Tuesday

Stephanie puffed up to the door with long tale about broken down moped. Sat her in warm kitchen with tea and adopted my pastoral manner. She'd come to write up the burglary, so I moved her to the study. Convinced her the theft of one video machine only needed a very small paragraph and no reference to Canon Hopkins. Didn't remind her of meeting of PCC on stained glass window.

Meeting very low key. One hour's talk about burglary then stained glass, Mothers and Toddlers' need for toys and Church cleaning crammed into half an hour. Stained glass abandoned in favour of new hanging lights in chancel Colin's wanted for ages. M & T group a 'great idea' bringing in young families, strengthening Sunday School etc. etc. – but can't they organise their own jumble sale for funds? There's a working party for annual Church Spring Clean next week. Ugh.

March 11 Wednesday

Sheep out again in drive. Shoved them back through hole in fence, rang Sam. He said why couldn't I do a quick repair.

Late for Lent lunch – hard, unleavened rolls and washing up water soup – left early for Mothers and Toddlers. Mums wanted to know about burglary. Discussed possible Jumble Sale. Mrs Turner (mother of ultra-neat child, Lisa and also only baby in world never to be dirty, smelly or sick) suggested just baby and toddler clothes. Mums enthusiastic – afraid I suspect Mrs Turner of wanting to show off her pristine used baby clothes. Sale next Wednesday.

March 12 Thursday

Anonymous letter arrived slamming Colin for refusing to baptise any babies. Saw Joe Wilson running down our drive and the note was so vitriolic it must be from his wife. Must sort her out tomorrow.

Sewing meeting. Usual farce of me appearing to preside while doing absolutely nothing. Members don't seem to mind – treat me like a mascot. Give me simple jobs to do and watch with amusement while I mess them up. Took all afternoon to cover a coat hanger with pink material, didn't finish (what sort of person uses covered coat hangers?) Everyone else making clothes, embroidering tablecloths, creating toys and perfecting patchwork quilts to sell for Church funds. Group also passes on lots of facts about parishioners – illnesses, golden weddings, exam and sport successes, who's moving or losing a job, who is related to whom and why it's no good asking Mrs Thingummy to join because she fell out with the Vicar before the Vicar before last and hasn't darkened a religious door since.

Mrs Wilson's Note

Dear Editor,

What about suffer the little children to come unto me? Our vicar apparently thinks he knows better than Jesus and turns away poor innocents. Of course he's quick enough to encourage those scruffy louts from the council estate into the youth group when their parents never come to Church. I wonder he can stand there and read the Holy Scriptures week after week in his fancy robes that are more like the Catholics than decent Church of England. I say he'll end up with no decent people left.

Signed, A Well Wisher

March 13 Friday

Visited the Wilsons. She amazed to see me. Gentle probe approach. Just as well. Out it all came after two hours and four cups of tea each. Her atheist father refused to have her baptised – she didn't live anywhere near here then – but had to 'get it done' on the insistence of the Vicar in order to get married to Joe. Dreadful row with her parents – mother died a week later, father blamed Mrs Wilson and never forgave her. Mrs Wilson tried to get her own daughter baptised but vicar refused to baptise infants. Whole family moved here. Daughter now an unmarried mum and non Churchgoer and the child still unbaptised. I offered Colin's services wholesale – weddings, baptisms etc. No response. Suggested daughter joins Mothers and Toddlers. Slight slackening of Wilson facial muscles. 'Grans welcome too,' I said. Actually a Wilson smile. Later she asked me to tear up her letter as she's misunderstood Colin. If I could get her to M & T she could make the teas, but I didn't mention that. Better to quit while I was ahead.

Easter anthem going reasonably well. Derek plays it faster than it should go to get it over with. Joyce nearly said something about this, but changed her mind.

March 14 Saturday

Youth Group chaos until Derek said magic word 'outing'. Christopher Bowels and Jason Fearns stopped kicking football about. All seven girls stopped chanting 'boring, boring.' 'Where?', they all asked suspiciously, obviously thinking it sounded too good to be true. I panicked. 'Ice skating,' said Dennis. Deathly silence. (Ice skating? The rink's an hour away. Transport? Money? I thought) 'Alright then,' 'Yeah,' 'How much?' they said. 'In a fortnight £3' said Dennis. He'll contact parents. 'Then what?' they asked. 'You say.' All wanted to go on as before (boys kicking ball into village; girls giggling, falling out, making it up, daring each other to speak to the boys). Dennis said nothing. Then they decided that, put baldly like that, it all sounded boring. Why couldn't they . . . Dennis took it all down, only stopping when they'd said enough to last two years. Some of it daft (abseiling, pop concert with famous group). The rest I could see Dennis's mind working on.

Colin said we don't usually have outings in Lent. I set upon him – youth work more important than silly rules, didn't deserve to have a Youth Group and a new dynamic leader etc. etc. He said he'd only been going to say he thought this was a case for an exception. Exit deflated wife.`

CHAPTER FOUR

WRONG IMPRESSIONS

March 15 Sunday

Joyce v Derek feud makes Church music unpredictable. Derek's abandoned his Selections From Shows and plays Joyce's proper voluntaries fast and with a beat I'm sure the composers would be surprised about.

March 16 Monday

Writing this shakily in bed between fevered naps – but I'm not dead yet despite persistent rumours in village. Had a disagreement with large lorry while cycling hurriedly to shops. Lorry's back wheel caught me as it turned a corner too close to the kerb, threw me in the air in a neat somersault. Landed in the road, minus clump of hair and dignity, but I was unconscious so didn't care. Someone bundled me into ambulance and I came to in Casualty with Colin standing over me. Nothing broken or seriously damaged – sent home to bed. Total stranger saw Colin in clerical gear standing over me in road, thought it was any old casualty having benefit of last rites and spread story of fatal accident. Fortunately children only heard it from Colin.

Archdeacon rang to offer condolences and a Requiem Mass. Told him politely he was being a bit previous. Colin toured village with story of my miraculous escape. Don't think they'll believe it until they see me. Bicycle in cycle shop, sadly twisted. Painkillers beginning to work – feel very drows . . .

March 17 Tuesday

All day in and out of fevered sleep peopled with giant lorries that changed into ducks and sheep. I ache. Woke at 11pm when Colin came to bed. I insisted I was going to Mothers and Toddles tomorrow to organise Bring and Buy and welcome Mrs Wilson and family. Mumbled about food and doing the washing.

March 18 Wednesday

Woke at 11am, much better. Next time I woke it was 2pm. Tried to get up for M & T, had to give up. Oh well, I'll have to start again with Mrs Wilson – if ever I can get up from this bed. Colin came at 4pm to say Mrs Wilson had sent flowers and message that she'd made teas for M & T and her daughter wanted to see Colin – or it may have been Mrs Wilson wanted her daughter to see Colin. Same thing. Baileys visited me. Dennis organising cars for Youth Group outing and reduced rates for rinks. Not to worry if I didn't feel like going.

Worried about food and washing. Colin said they were managing – made him promise he wouldn't accept help that involved anyone going near uncleaned cooker. Church cleaning was due this week – almost worth the accident not to have to do it. Colin might have said they'd postponed it until I got better – but I hope that was me being delirious.

March 19 Thursday

Skulking in bed doing nothing has to stop. Started work on poems for Good Friday afternoon for people to read in a service. Decided to make it Thoughts On The Seven Last Words. Quite pleased with it, then got stuck and in any case fell asleep.

Stephanie visited, got out her notebook. That girl's beginning to resemble an angel of doom. Sat her on edge of bed and probed into her private life. Doesn't seem to have any.

March 20 Friday

Got it! The end of that verse I was writing yesterday. I've never been so far ahead of myself for Good Friday. Think I owe it to the lorry driver to forgive him for the accident.

Colin really chuffed about Wilson daughter and baby both being baptised. Said I'd done a good job – and I haven't even met the girl yet.

Must get up soon – magazine, Youth Group, Sunday School etc. etc. Newspaper had a brief piece about accident – Stephanie should know my Christian name by now. Geoffrey rang, apologising for not having asked after me but hadn't realised it had happened until he read it in the paper. Joyce popped in on way to choir practice to say not to worry about anthem. So did Derek. Amazing. He's notorious for never noticing when anyone's ill. Has been known to enquire after people he finally missed about three months after they'd died and having played at their funeral. Got up for several hours – weak but determined. Children and Colin asked if I knew washing machine was broken. It's not. Just idiosyncratic from being about seventh hand. They just cursed it (Colin) or kicked it (children) and spent fortune at launderette. I felt smug when I got it to go. It's nice to have a rare talent.

March 21 Saturday

Cycle shop sent back my bike – in pieces in cardboard box. Useful for spares, Colin said, and put it in outhouse. Spares for what? My cycling days are definitely over. Did shaky pedestrian tour of village to assure everyone I was alright.

March 22 Sunday

At Church surrounded by well wishers and those curious to see if any spectacular bruises and abrasions are visible. Some are. Christopher brought me a gift box tied with pink ribbon. How nice, I thought. It contained a slow-worm and its babies – part of three year campaign to discover which creepy crawlies send me into hysterics. Quite a lot do, but I've perfected internal screams invisible to the public eye. Scrapped my lesson and talked about Being Kind To People, aimed at Christopher. He said did fellow beings include snakes and if so why wasn't a lovely pet as good a present as flowers?

Recruited volunteers for Good Friday readings – still ahead of myself. It can't last.

March 23 Monday

Colin said at breakfast did I remember we were going to Gillian Newton's 21st birthday party in hall tonight? (Bet someone reminded him first). Panic stations. Present! Card! Niggling feeling all morning about hall.

Produce Association Chairman rang lunch time to ask for heat in hall for annual meeting tonight. Assumed Colin alright for presenting prizes as he was asked in December (Just got to get secretary for that hall.) Talked Mr Webb into moving meeting from seven o'clock to six. Told Mrs Newton I'd help her prepare hall at 7pm. Told Colin he was presenting prizes at 6pm – cross but agreed. Told wedding couple he was going to see at 6pm that they'd have to wait until tomorrow – emergency in parish, I said. All went like clockwork.

March 24 Tuesday

Church cleaning (Don't remember Theological College mentioning anything about Vicar's wife kneeling on Church path thumping hassocks – and do Vicar's husbands have to do the same?) Wore dreadful clothes and cloth round my head. Primary school children passed on nature walk commenting loudly on me 'saying prayers.' Stuck my tongue out at them – they giggled. Teacher looked startled – so did Anne and John, who I hadn't seen in the group.

Smartly dressed couple walked dog past and asked about services – sounded off about death of Matins, language of TV ads now used in Church instead of Authorised Version and rubbishy new hymns. After three hours of cleaning, feeling filthy and aching from accident bruises, I told them sharply that Matins was dreary, the Bible was for everyone not erudite few and if they came they'd hear proper hymns. Man said he'd speak to Vicar about insolence of cleaning staff and left. Arthur (inside porch doing light tidying of notice board) glad to see me talking to new couple in Miss Cavendish's old house. Mr and Mrs Bessant. Weren't they nice people? I said I'd not had chance to get to know them but would call later. Secretly jettisoned 14 tatty hymn and prayer books.

Went home, had bath, washed hair, dressed in best Vicar's wife kit and went to Bessants' house – they delighted to have Vicar's wife call. Cups of tea, biscuits, family photos, plans to turn fantastic cottage into grotty executive home and 'become part of village community'. Sorry to have to mention frightful cleaning woman at Church, very rude, thought Padre ought to know. I promised to tell him. Told Bessant he'd love our traditional Evensong and apologised for occasional chorus at Eucharist – sorry Holy Communion – to please Sunday School. He said he and his 'lady wife' were 'as good Christians as those once-a-week types' and would choose Evensong, harvest, Christmas and, of course, Remembrance Sunday for their Church parades. Didn't ask which armed service he'd graced.

March 25 Wednesday.

Mother and Toddler sale took £30. Mrs Wilson made children take turns to use favourite toys. One mum stormed off when son deprived of talking telephone – I had to patch things up and try to make Mrs Wilson stay with the teapot. (Do they give Nobel Peace Prize for parish work?) Mrs Wilson's daughter a nice girl – wants to marry baby's father but he's a belligerent Trades Unionist and mum's against. Told Colin.

March 26 Thursday

Gave talk to next village's Women's Fellowship on The Role Of The Vicar's Wife Today. So boring three older members asleep before half way point so I finished abruptly, took early tea break and hastily organised trivia quiz. Much better. Chairman, who must have slept throughout, gave prepared speech saying she had no idea a clergyman's wife's duties were so complex.

Colin says Pamela Wilson wants to marry as soon as mum agrees.

March 27 Friday

In Church found strange middle-aged, vague looking woman in battered straw hat putting two arrangements with two blooms and a lump of dead greenery on the Altar – in Lent! I said how lovely and was it a special occasion. They're for this afternoon's funeral of her brother. I remembered Colin saying about two recluses in gloomy house down Park Road. Milkman broke in. Man dead, no other relatives. Colin and undertakers organised funeral. Woman in sort of trance, kept talking to me about bouquets. Helped her finish arrangements (not much improvement). Walked her home. She shouted at me not to interfere, slammed herself in house.

Neighbour appeared saying did I know she'd just murdered her brother and was going to be locked up? Colin said it was wonderful she'd ventured into Church but it was a pity I'd upset her. Now he'd have to persuade her out again for the funeral.

He did persuade her out but it took him an hour. She's back inside again defying an army of Colin, doctors and assorted health, social and council workers. Think the next talk I give will be called How Vicar's Wives Can't Do Anything Right. Told Dennis I could manage the ice rink tomorrow.

March 28 Saturday

I may never move again. But I think we can truthfully say we're into proper youth work. My car load – Lesley, Tamar, Clare – very good except when demanding gooey ices and fizzy drinks on way home. Told them the first one sick would get out and walk. No one ever knows when I mean things – not even me – so no one was sick.

At rink I went on in excruciating boots to look after everyone. Clung to side throughout. Everyone else skated very professionally in middle, except Dennis, who laughed at me so much his face went purple. Cut my hand when falling, pressed First Aid button for help. Alarm bell went all over the building, skaters stopped and three staff came, shouting orders about an ambulance. Cross at false alarm. Dennis laughed some more. All enjoyed it – but what next? Actor friend of Dennis doing a drama workshop. Colin is finally converted. Dennis is officially a 'good find'.

March 29 Sunday

Tamar said she was sick as soon as she got home, but had a great time and would I put her down for the walk. Walk? Now that is where Dennis is on his own, and I told him so. He said I could stay behind and do refreshments. He has three parents lined up to help.

Today one of my preaching sprees. Colin always sticks me in front on Mothering Sunday to 'say a few words'. Went on about little ways to make mum feel appreciated. Shouldn't think it had much effect. Saw one child screaming at her mum afterwards and Anne and John said did I really want to be woken up with cups of tea all the time. I said no.

March 30 Monday

Colin had spending day off – bought me a fairly new bike. Managed a trip round garden but couldn't face traffic. John and Anne took me out on roads – one in front and one behind. Stanley saw us, fell about laughing. Whole village seemed to hold its breath as we negotiated dread accident corner and gasped when a lorry passed us.

March 31 Tuesday

Went to see Bessants to report to Miss Cavendish on what's happening to her house as didn't really take it in last time. On second thoughts, don't think I'll tell her about the cocktail cabinet.

Bessants fitting into community really well, they said. He's on Produce Association committee already. Said he'd heard about cock up –'beg pardon, ladies present' – over hall bookings. What's needed is efficient chappie to run hall. Mrs Bessant secretly asked me to offer him the job. Said I'd speak to Colin about it. After all, it could be interesting seeing him deal with Leonard. Like lighting a firework and retiring to a safe distance while it smoulders. I should have to have a bucket of water handy though. Colin said 'good idea.' Bessant's military experience would be invaluable. Perhaps I shouldn't have mentioned the offer.

Told Miss Cavendish they were caring for her little house. She didn't believe me – she's met them – but she's perfectly happy and a great friend of Joyce. Now I come to think of it, she kept smiling knowingly when I mentioned Joyce. Strange.

Letter From Mrs Bessant To Her Married Daughter

Dear Patricia,

Please do not worry about Daddy and I in our new home. Daddy had become so upset at the lowering of the tone of the area that the doctor thought moving was the only way to avoid serious illness, even though it meant being a long way from you and the children. He is much better already, although perhaps it would be advisable not to bring the children and Toby to visit yet as I feel he is not ready yet for Toby's clever witticisms and he still doesn't understand why you won't let him pay for a proper education for the children at his old school.

I really think Daddy is going to settle down here and we might even be able to go to Church now he has found out that they are not too high and a very nice class of people goes to Evensong. I thought he was going to have one of his funny turns when a cleaning lady at the Church was very rude to him, but the Vicar's wife quite won him over – such a respectable person and calling so soon with promises to discipline the 'offender'. Daddy should take over their hall management. It is in such chaos apparently that it should provide him with an outlet for months. Perhaps, if he really finds a niche here, he will be able to spare me to come to you on a short visit. He would send his love I know, but has gone to a meeting of the Produce Association which, he says, needs someone to get it into shape. Love to you all, Mummy.

CHAPTER FIVE

THE GOOD FIGHT

April 1 Wednesday

Quite a wag, Stanley. At Lent Lunch told me he'd seen sheep grazing round war memorial. Colin hadn't arrived (gets later the fouler the soup – this week chick pea). I dashed to the scene – no sheep. Must Stanley April Fool me every year? I had last laugh. Took so long hunting for sheep, Mrs Fearns made him finish the soup instead of me.

Mothers and Toddlers – Mrs Wilson trapped me in kitchen to tell of 'great sacrifice' of letting Pamela marry her yob 'for the sake of my grandchild.' Wants big Church wedding – no problem. Wants wedding Holy Saturday – big problem. Colin's only person in Christendom still calling it that – everyone else says Easter Saturday – and still refusing to marry people then. I bravely explained it to Mrs Wilson, who raged about Romish practices and selfish clergy. I had brilliant idea – told her no flowers in Church until Easter Sunday. Well! Wedding without flowers scarcely legal. Uneasy peace declared.

Colin agreed on Saturday after Easter. Then I remembered we're going to Margaret's from Easter Monday for a week's holiday. Muttered Leonard-type expletive and agreed we'd have to come back on the Friday – again. Sisters of clergy wives have to be long suffering.

April 2 Thursday

Nearly beat technology over magazine this month – computer work fine but printer cartridge ran out. Took all afternoon to find one, finished at midnight.

Colin depressed. One of Confirmation candidates changed his mind – Jason Fearns. 'There's eight left,' I said cheerily. Christopher Bowles always does what he does, Colin said. He'll probably drop out too. They're Sunday School kids so I went round to Jason's. Mrs Fearns child sitting for her son's children and experimenting with muesli bars. I ate three before she said it was no good trying to change Jason's mind. His mates at school found out about Confirmation and kept jeering. Tell him to be a brave soldier for Christ, I said. He was, she said. He beat up the gang leader and got detentions for a week from the head and clout round head from boy's father. If that's how God treats His soldiers he's going to join another army, Jason says. Concept of passive resistance I judged too complicated to explain to a young lad through a third party really only interested in muesli bars, so I left.

April 3 Friday

Colin found (under heap of papers I finally moved from kitchen table) invitation to us to Induction tonight of chap to a nearby parish. RSVP long past. Got me to ring churchwarden and accept (after all my fault. Hadn't found way of laying table without moving things left on it).

What to do about choir practice? Anthem ragged, Good Friday hymns not yet tried. Asked Derek to take practice – he panicked. I suggested asking Joyce to help. Panicked some more. I asked her anyway. She said not to worry.

Bishop's sermon at Induction just as good as last three times I've heard it. Legal bits boring. New Incumbent lumbered with reputation as 'dynamic' with 'new ideas'. They're all said to be that at first – way of making sure congregation's so terrified of having to pass the peace and do liturgical dance in the aisle they'll accept modest change gratefully. This man's been a journalist so perhaps they're right this time. Refreshments no better than ours on similar occasions, I'm glad to say. New man and Stephanie got on well. Now that could be a good match.

April 4 Saturday

Heard from Pat (over freezer chest at supermarket) choir practice 'thorough' – she and other descants kept an extra hour over three awkward bars. Didn't ask what her husband thought about it. Being a 'religion has done more harm in the world than anything else' merchant he barely allows her to come to Church and drives her to and fro to prevent her being beholden to anyone. Glad I wasn't there as I only get top A on a good day with the wind behind me and being relegated to second soprano by someone I recruited myself less than three months ago would be megga embarrassing (Anne's phrase).

April 5 Sunday

Choir practice after service at Joyce's request – our Sunday dinner late and in our household that's a sin on a par with not honouring father and mother and coveting neighbour's oxen.

Jason Fearns not in Church. Colin really worried. I said he would probably return when all danger of being nagged into Confirmation was over and anyway he's still in youth group. Christopher Bowles still lined up for Thursday – his family are more forceful.

April 6 Monday

Stephanie dropped in casually and I thought she might have heard about Jason's fight and be going to do Sunday School Lad Beat Up My Son. But no. She's fallen heavily for Whatshisname – new Vicar up the road – and pumped me about him while ostensibly checking details about Induction. Couldn't help her over the man's hobbies, views of marriage, state of romantic life and shoe size. Perhaps I'll ask him to dinner, pump him and pass on information. He might like the dark haired type with glasses and a moped. Asked him for Tuesday without telling Colin – he's bound to mutter 'Lent'. New man agreed, seemed pleased. His house built to fit Victorian cleric with 16 children and all he's got is two dogs. Must ask someone what his name is.

April 7 Tuesday

Coffee Morning here for Christian Aid. All arrived looking slightly dazed. Miss Cavendish plucked up courage to ask if I knew a man was shampooing sheep in our garden. I didn't but said loftily it was someone getting Sam's sheep ready for showing.

Heard Mr Bessant's making a stir in Produce Association. Wants them to have Ye Olde Englishe supper – game soup, steak and kidney pud, roly poly pud. They abandoned that five years ago due to excessive incidence of high blood pressure and heart problems in members and changed to salads. Voting between two meals now 50/50. Colin's speaking at supper and I'm going so I'm glad something interesting is happening to divert 40 people telling me about their prize dahlias and how evil judge robbed them of cup. Leonard's unnaturally quiet about Bessant's management of hall now I think of it. Something's up, I know it is.

Colin also subdued about dinner with whatshisname but that's due to Jason and Jason's mother blaming Colin for him backing out of Confirmation.

April 8 Wednesday

Mrs Wilson's organised wedding down to last vol-au-vent and arranging for baby to be farmed out to cousin 'so the happy couple can have a honeymoon.' Actually her next door neighbour told me it's because the baby's been kept a secret from lots of the family and they hope to produce it later and hope everyone will forget to do their sums.

Rehearsed Good Friday readings, sounded almost professional especially with Arthur and Anne.

April 9 Thursday

Confirmation moving, but long. Sermon long, seven hymns from A & M's turgid 200s, prayers long (knew they would be when a Reader marched to the back with several prayer books, most with bits of paper sticking out from pages). Christopher says he'll 'get' Jason for next time. Refreshments unnecessarily lavish I thought – six tons of sandwiches, two dozen quiches, five large cakes and assorted salads.

April 10 Friday

Practice. Derek definitely slower than he was and doesn't seem to be planning to play selections from Beatles as people arrive for Good Friday service. Pity – part of tradition now. Stephanie kept coming in half a beat too early or too late. Impervious to Joyce's 'looks'. Ain't love grand.

April 11 Saturday

Dennis's actor friend is blond youth the kids had actually *seen on television,* very fleetingly, in Casualty. Girls drooled. I did until he asked me if I could 'rustle up some coffee or cola or something.' There's a world of difference between being taken for granted as refreshment organiser by parish and by glamorous TV actor. Dennis saw me stamp off to put on dratted kettle and there he was again, laughing. Have to admit, had its funny side. Christopher had brought Jason. All lads suspicious of Jerry at first in case un-macho dancing or mime were involved. Warmed to it when they improvised a street brawl. All wanted to put on their play in Church during service. Knew I ought not to make excuses and refuse, so I didn't. Quite a daring decision for a mere tea lady I thought.

Jerry had to promise to return one day. Dennis came home and had deep theological discussion with Colin, mainly about no matter how weird the play was at least Jason was in it. I think Dennis forgot to mention Jason's part was actually type casting – punching someone.

April 12 Sunday

Palm Sunday. Oh well, at least Bessant and Leonard are firm friends and allies now – against me.

Congregation, including wheelchairs, arrived at hall for traditional ceremony of blessing of palms and procession of witness through street. I was late. Hall door firmly shut. Had forgotten to tell Bessant about it and he has key and doesn't come to Parish Communion. Ugly scene about to break over me so mumbled something about 'under new management – Leonard should have known.' Considerable feeling against both. Colin tried spreading Christian forbearance. No effect. Then collected palms from car, blessed them in street and started procession. Several said later it was more effective that way. Could we always do it like that. Still mutterings about Bessant and Leonard.

I'd just collapsed before TV when Colin ushered in Bessant and Leonard. Both polite but puzzled. People blaming them for forgetting something they knew nothing about. I feigned amazement. They suspected me and always will, but calmed down over coffee. As I say – useful alliance formed.

April 13 Monday

Washing machine broke for good while trying to cope with choir and clergy robes, altar line etc. for Easter (why do I have to do it? – because my predecessor did, that's why). Flooded utility room. Mopped up. Spent hours at launderette. Ironing it when tramp came for food. Got him some. Really wanted to talk over business and matrimonial troubles. I forgot iron. Surplice not too scorched if you don't look closely.

Began house cleaning for whatshisname dinner tomorrow. Colin's also forgotten his name. Rang his churchwarden who said either Wilton or Watson, Brian or Barry. Do I detect a touch of disillusion with their new Vicar already?

April 14 Tuesday

All day cleaning, getting food ready. Tramp came back. Said the Methodists let him sleep in a shed and didn't like to ask for food as well. Another episode of his story, then quick choir practice. Surprised food got cooked.

Came clean with whatshisname, asked his name. Bernard Walton. He was relieved as he'd forgotten ours. Nice enough but going too fast. True the bonfire is best place for their hymn book but better not to say so straightaway. Especially without finding out who gave them 50 years ago when it was the present churchwarden's mother. Also true, hymn sandwich service brings in more young families. Scrapping Evensong for it looses entire evening congregation. More older people than young – net gain two mothers, four children: loss, 17 Evensongers. Back to the drawing board.

What he needed, I quipped, was a wife. Colin choked over lemon sorbet. Me advocating parochial enslavement of women? Bernard agreed – eagerly. Stephanie, you're on your way. Don't blow it. If I fix him up with Stephanie, he'll be too busy worrying about her problems to worry about his own.

April 15 Wednesday

It seems I'm to be Bed and Breakfast to waifs and strays. Colin's offered our spare room to new young woman teacher beginning at the Comprehensive in town next term, until she finds something permanent. Nice girl, said Colin. Church goer. Did I mind? Too busy to worry really. She'll have to put up with odd furniture in room and learn to live in a mad house. Visitors to us meanwhile will have to use camp beds in old playroom and hang clothes on floor. Was going to use that room for office, between mini snooker and dolls house. Never mind.

Penance over last Lent Lunch this year. Mrs Fearns had cold and asked me to take over cooking her borsch. Ugh. Bought large tins of tomato and oxtail, mixed them together with dregs of sherry. Several congratulated me, asked for recipe. I said it was secret, but I had a lovely one for borsch.

April 16 Maundy Thursday

Father-in-law came. Forgot he was coming, hastily prepared spare room. He spent most of day practising bass for anthem. Every man's voice welcome. I sloshed lots of starch over an ancient surplice. It looks alright from a distance and away from light.

Mr Bessant arrived as we were leaving for service to ask about his wife doing Easter flowers. Seemed amazed anyone should go to Church on Maundy Thursday – except Queen for Maundy Money, of course. Told him hastily his wife could do window opposite door.

Went back to do my silent vigil in Church 10pm – 11pm. Just three of us. Amazing what creaks and scufflings you hear. Wonderful to sit and think without fear of interruption. Couldn't bear to leave so stayed till midnight. Forgot I'd left hot cross buns dough in airing cupboard. Rescued it from the shelves where it had crept. Finished making them at 1.30pm.

April 17 Good Friday

Buns looked strange, tasted OK. Meant to go to Meditation 1pm – 2pm but undertaker rang to say Mrs Miles' husband dead. Colin in Church so I went round there. Didn't do much. It's not struck her yet. Cycled like wind to Church, two minutes to spare before readings. No time to explain lateness. Everyone looked annoyed. All went well. Readers wonderful, hymns good. Running ten minutes short so Colin preached slowly, put in more prayers. Finished on dot of 3pm.

Remembered Sunday School and youth group due to decorate Easter garden and Church porch tomorrow. Tramped fields for moss and greenery. Wish I could recall if anyone does window I told Mr Bessant his wife could do.

April 18 Holy Saturday

Overslept. At Church only few daffs left. Our garden has even fewer. Moss gone brown, forgot to sprinkle overnight. Four Sunday School children running amok among litter of flowers, greenery, vases and Easter garden figures. Another year when I didn't get round to painting their chipped faces and clothes – figures I mean, not children.

Mr Bessant snapping military style at wife arranging daffodils like guardsmen. Mrs Clampet crying in choir vestry. She's done Bessants' window 12 years in memory of dead husband, bought £20 worth of flowers for the purpose. Couldn't understand how mix up happened. I didn't tell her. None of youth group there so told her to do porch – bigger space, more important position etc. She cheered up. But no pots left. Told her to keep an eye on Sunday School, cycled home for ten of ours (people give them to us thinking Vicarage ought to have masses of beautifully arranged flowers – never use them). Got back, only one kid left, others gone home for lunch.

Colin said hadn't heart to tell Mrs Miles he couldn't do funeral Friday because we're gadding about (going to visit my sister) – so we're coming back Thursday. Wonderful. And did I want to leave Tuesday to avoid Bank Holiday traffic? No, I didn't!

April 19 Easter Sunday

Crucifer in procession to bless Easter garden realised we'd forgotten to roll away the stone and hastily did it. Total lack of grave clothes inside sepulchre. Ruined symbolism, Colin said later. Shaky start to anthem. Joyce gave us a 'look' – we improved no end. Derek held out until coffee time before giving us a selection from Le Miserables, Joyce smiled faintly. Congregation showered us with Easter eggs. I praised Mrs Clampet profusely for porch decoration. She says she'll always do it at future festivals as it gives 'more scope'. She was the only one acknowledged as I forgot to remind Colin to thank the others.

Colin alarmed Jason not there. Christopher said not to worry as it's a good sign. Jason felt awkward at not communicating —but leave it to him. We agreed.

Colin's sermon very good but he looked tired. I insisted we packed tonight for early start tomorrow.

April 20 Monday

Well, it was early for us. All ready by 8am. Father-in-law had taxi to station to save detour. Just as we were locking doors, phone rang. *I answered it.* Miss Cavendish saying neighbour had fallen, in hospital urgently calling for Vicar – certainly for first time in her life. Colin went. Stayed two hours.

When he got back, I shouted. Felt guilty so I sulked for 50 miles. Then I recognised landmarks and cheered up. Traffic better than expected. Made up at least an hour.

Margaret and Co all well, full of village news, family gossip. New kitchen to admire. Meant to have good moan about telephone never stopping, parish, Bessants, Leonard, Johnson, Diocese, Mothers and Toddlers, Sunday School, stained glass window, Wilson wedding, Archdeacon, Rural Dean . . . forgot it all. Tried to persuade some of tribe to come and stay with us, then remembered we were expecting lodger soon. But she won't stay long. Will she?

April 23 Thursday

Put off starting for home as long as possible. All subdued on journey. I wish we lived nearer. Perhaps we will one day, although probably not until we retire. Parishes round Margaret are so low. Colin would either change them in six weeks, upset everyone and have to leave or try to change himself, fail – and have to leave.

Amazingly, no note from Arthur breaking bad news. Usually when we return someone's ill or dead or Church boiler's blown up.

CHAPTER SIX

YOU CAN'T BE SERIOUS

April 24 Friday

Colin forgot to tell Arthur we were returning Thursday. Arthur's note arrived this morning. Leonard and Bessant had row over who should provide loo rolls for hall. Leonard said if Bessant so keen on everything being correct he could clean the entire ***ing hall himself. Bessant said if any corporal had spoken to him like that he'd have been slammed in the cooler. Leonard resigned. Bessant said that was good as the man was probably a Commiagitator. It was a long note. Colin wished, aloud, that Bessant hadn't been asked to run the hall. And anyway he hadn't time to deal with such things. And he went off to the funeral.

I braved Leonard's tongue by going to his home. Miraculously he's quite different there. His wife says 'Leonard' sternly when he begins a swear word and he changes it to something innocuous. But he won't come back unless Bessant goes. I caved in. Bessant must go. Went round and told him. He said he and Mrs Bessant felt our services were 'too close to Rome' so they'd be going 'elsewhere' to Mattins. Didn't like to say the nearest had been at Bernard's parish and he's scrapped it. Mrs Bessant rang later in tears. Husband out organising dog's walkies. Begged me to give him back the job. Apparently he's very kind and thoughtful at heart. I mustn't take offence at his 'unfortunate manner.' I said she'd have to clear it with Leonard. She said she'd have a go.

Note From Arthur

Dear All,

I hope you had a refreshing break after the rigours of the Easter Festival.

I'm afraid I have a couple of items of bad news. Old Mrs Norman from the sheltered housing passed away on Monday. Her daughter said the old lady was glad Colin had been able to spare her a few minutes before dashing off on his holiday but the family were distressed that he could not be with her when she died. As I expect you know, the daughter found it difficult to visit the old lady more than a couple of times a year as she is a business executive and has her career to think of. She could not come to the hospital herself as she was at a very important meeting. I expect she'll soon be in touch over her wishes for the funeral which she has arranged with the undertaker for next Monday. I felt it impolite to mention your day off as it seemed to be the only time she could spare.

Mr Bessant and Leonard are finding it difficult to work together over the hall. Mr Bessant feels that Leonard's manner is too abrasive when asked to carry out certain essential duties and I understand from Leonard's wife – she said Leonard was 'too distressed' to talk to me himself – that Leonard feels disgruntled at Mr Bessant's applying a stricter regime than he is used to.

Perhaps now you are back one of you could try to pour oil on troubled waters as it were.

April 25 Saturday

Well Pamela's married in the eyes of the Church, but not really of her mother and Mothers and Toddlers may have to find a new tea lady. I went to the wedding out of curiosity. Bridegroom like most bridegrooms in new suit, concentrating on not loosening his tie under pressure. Pamela wore restrained spring dress. Cousin looked after baby miles away (Baptism in a fortnight).

Colin, despite couple's circumstances, insisted on his usual custom of leaving bride and bridegroom on their own for a few minutes in vestry after service. Then opened vestry door, organ started Wedding March. Nothing. Colin puzzled – then alarmed. Happy couple had vanished, leaving note. Reception too much – gone away. Love to baby. I left hastily – my mirth not really appropriate then. When I returned, more or less recovered from giggles, found everyone going for Colin – some physically. I hurried among them, muttering 'urgent call from the hospital.' Whisked him away. Heard later from Doris at paper shop they all went ahead with reception. Alarming stories of bridegroom's secret past as a wanted felon circulating. I reminded village, through Doris, that, apart from four day union conference in

Scarborough, he'd been present in the village since he was born with the same legal status as his own baby. Sensed an atmosphere of disappointment.

Youth Group, including Jason, rehearsed play for tomorrow. Modern language Passion and Resurrection with police arriving amid sounds of sirens and rounding up of disciples. Jesus dies in electric chair. Sensational news headlines. They put heart and soul into it. Hope people appreciate it. Dennis said not to worry. Next youth event, barbecue in our garden. I expect I'll do the food.

Hope Pamela and husband enjoying themselves. Wonder where they've gone. India? Greek village? African Safari?'

Note Left By Pamela

Sorry mum, it's all a bit too much – the reception, photos and everything. Have gone away quietly, back in a few weeks. Have a good time at the reception and save some cake for us. Tell the Vicar thanks for giving us the chance to escape.

Love Pamela

PS Tell Beatie thanks for looking after Baby and to buy what she needs. We'll settle up when we get back.

April 26 Sunday

Dennis right not to worry. Bemused congregation loved the play. Miss Cavendish couldn't exactly work out what it meant, but would resist to the death their right to perform it. Jason left after portraying a particularly brutal policeman. Christopher said not to worry. Colin pleased not to have to apologise for youth group. Derek thrilled because they asked him to play theme tune from The Bill. Joyce glad we'd made a 'positive response to criticism.'

April 27 Monday

Remembered to get printer cartridge. Hope PCC coughs up the money.

We bought washing machine. Very complicated but I'll work out average programme and ignore rest (bet no machine invented can remove iron mould from surplices living in vestry cupboards since the Reformation or grease from candles spilt down choir robes).

Went to bed. Remembered while dozing over a book that teacher arrives tomorrow. Got up, hoovered floor, changed sheets, tidied up. Colin and children slept through it all.

April 28 Tuesday

Judith and I going to get on. Red hair, freckles, late twenties, trifle eccentric. Told her to use whole house and have family meals. She offered us use of her car, self as sitter for children. Anne annoyed at need for sitter but won over by offers of lifts to cinema, friends' houses etc. when mean parents too busy.

I think Stephanie's got problems. 'Her' Bernard Walton came and took instant shine to Judith, hung on every word. Stephanie must act quickly. How shall I tell her? She'd be a lot less of a nuisance as a clergy wife and Judith's too brimming with vitality for that job. I used to think I was! Oh well. Bernard's going to youth leaders' seminar next week. I was but I'll get Stephanie to go instead. Judith and Bernard both fanatical about cricket and old cars. And antiques. Poor Stephanie.

Colin said Joyce volunteered to take over hall management, appoint own cleaning staff. He must have got it wrong. She just wouldn't do any of that – unless she has an ulterior motive.

April 29 Wednesday

Leonard, and Bessant arrived simultaneously, pursued by sheep who had escaped again. Had to decide between asking two furious men to help round up sheep or leave same two together in house while I rounded up the animals. Asked the two in, left them, rounded up sheep. Calmed down ducks.

Two men sitting uncomfortably on edge of armchairs, absorbed in conversation. They asked if it was true that this ***ing woman (not sure who used worst language) was interfering in running 'their' hall. Yes, I said, but all the same in Church of England these days, ***ing women everywhere. Both blamed women's libbers and female padres. I was ignored for ten minutes so rang Joyce at her college to get her to change her mind about taking over. 'Just what I thought,' she said in smug tone. 'Fighting each other until they're threatened and then ganging up.' 'You mean you knew it would happen like that?' I said. 'Life's one big playground,' she said and hung up. Bessant's the manager – Leonard's the cleaner and they went off to celebrate a famous victory over the monstrous regiment of women.

Judith asked to have 'a few friends' round tomorrow. I suggested she used dining room for privacy. Not that sort of gathering, she said.

Rang Stephanie. She wasn't keen on seminar until I mentioned Bernard was going and how well he was getting on with new lodger. She said she'd go. Didn't tell her they need packed lunch because Bernard doesn't know either so perhaps they can go to a pub together.

Letter To Bernard From His Mother

Dear Bernard

Are you sure you're alright in that cold old house? You know I could easily come down as your housekeeper. I could sell up here and then whatever parish you were in it would feel more like home. You would also not have problems with the 'spinsters of this parish' as Revd Atkinson had here before he had to leave over that business with choir girls on the annual outing. I noticed one or two females trying to catch your attention at the Induction. You'd think they would have more respect. I should keep yourself to yourself dear and, if you need a woman's touch with flower arranging etc., ask someone like that mousy person – Samantha something – who I met at the Induction and who won't be likely to make advances.

It was nice of that Vicar's wife to invite you to dinner dear, but be careful. Make sure the husband is always there because these middle aged women can be very dangerous to a man in your position.

I don't think you need go to that youth thing you spoke of. Youths in youth clubs are so scruffy and ill mannered. Get one of your parishioners to go. Our dear Vicar – not the present Incumbent with his appalling jeans and trainers but Revd Marsh

– used to say he was saving himself for Sundays 'and never got involved with parishioners' problems or what he called the 'social workers' domain' and we had a very nice class of person in Church in his day.

I'll come over as soon as dear Dr Day says my heart can stand it. Don't leave off your vests until June.

Love Mummy

PS That mousy girl's name is Stephanie.

April 30 Thursday

Judith's meeting was dozen or so friends in glittering collection of vintage cars. She's in Austin 7 Club and a friend brought her car out of storage. All stood prodding it and tinkering with engines of assembled cars and starting them up to alarm of our garden creatures. Meeting of Deanery clergy here same time. Their cars boxed in. Later demanded to be let out. Bernard with them, looking as though he wished he wasn't. Vintage car lot went off for drive. Judith asked me to go in hers. I got in, waved to astonished Rural Dean and Co and departed. Pretty hair raising. Road visible from beneath my feet. All pulled into pub car park, caused sensation. I desperately tried to look part of racy, young scene. Stanley walked up and asked if we were Sunday School outing. Exit Vicar's wife's street cred.

None of woolly scarved young men seemed particularly close to Judith – all treated her like sister. Good news for Bernard, bad for Stephanie. Colin said I should have stayed and chatted to the clergy instead of roaring off.

May 1 Friday

A breakthrough! Women's Hour Grupenfuhrer, Mrs Cottee, rang to ask me to give them 'a little talk'. Their speaker – 'What To Do With A Glut Of Strawberries' – gone down with food poisoning. I made no comment on that – honestly. Asked if they wanted my Praying Through Housework, Caring With Cakes or TV – Friend Or Foe? 'Nothing frightfully serious,' she said in horror. 'There's altogether too much theology and workshops on prayer these days.' Forgot to ask when and where it was – I'm sure they keep changing dates and times to avoid gatecrashing by praying riff raff. I'm going to put piece in magazine about my visit – so there. It's ridiculous having Church group run like Mafia. Told Colin. He said he was sure it served its purpose. So, he's afraid of them too (Mrs Cottee wife of former Tory agent of the no-politics-in-Church variety).

May 2 Saturday

Pamela Wilson-as-was back, paper shop's Doris told me. No tan. They went to Brighton – probably posed as unmarried for old times' sake. Pamela came round to ask what to do about mother. (Fortunately I had no time to answer between her sobs and broken sentences). Mum has kidnapped baby from distant relatives. Refuses to give it up to such irresponsible parents. New husband threatening militant action. Pamela sometimes thinks mum's right, sometimes thinks it rough to have provided baby with father and now have no baby, sometimes doesn't think, just cries. Escorted her home then visited Mrs Wilson. Kept waiting on doorstep with diatribe against daughter, son-in-law, daft clergyman who encouraged them. I feigned ignorance of everything, said only wanted to discuss baby's Baptism. Said she'd be perfect godmother – I lied, I lied. Nearly added we'd enter her in a Perfect Grandmother contest, but thought that probably going over the top. Invited in to tea. She 'only wanted good of baby,' tried to bring up Pamela to be good girl, did I want to see photos? Finally I was allowed to take baby back to Pamela. More tears, baby unmoved.

Family tea very late. Colin agreed to carry out everything I'd promised he would, even giving poor mite hideous middle name after Mrs Wilson's great grandmother.

May 3 Sunday

Colin announced meeting of Christian Aid Committee tomorrow. How did he know? I'm the organiser and I'd forgotten. Joyce had asked if we were doing anything for Christian Aid Week Monday week, that's how.

May 4 Monday

About a dozen CA collectors short to cover the whole place. Disaster as we've just got to make sure Bernard's parish doesn't raise more than we do this year – again. Forgot where I put huge box of Christian Aid collecting envelopes, publicity material, posters, display boards when it came months ago. Bound to turn up so I didn't tell committee. Decided to hold Cake Stall in hall.

May 5 Tuesday

Baileys, Joyce and new woman who sits at the back of Church and whose name I've forgotten agreed to do collecting. Nothing for it – had to ask Bessants. He refused – for both – as 'charity begins at home, I always say' – until asked to be in charge of giving out envelopes. Was I right? Is this the end of house to house collecting as we know it? Judith said she and three friends willing. Leaves me with two roads. (I hate it. I hate it). Plastered posters about.

Telephone Call From Mrs Cottee To Her Friend Madge

Madge   *Did you see the piece in the magazine?*

Mrs C   *Yes. No . . nothing to do with me, I assure you.*

Madge   *Overheard something, I suppose. She's always chatting to that person, Doris, in the paper shop. Then decided to put us among the youth groups and jumble sales.*

Mrs C   *Well, not exactly.*

Madge   *Not exactly?*

Mrs C   *She may have thought it alright, that is – er – I rang and asked her to speak to us. Hello, Madge. Are you still there?*

Madge   *You asked her to be our speaker, you mean? Give a talk?*

Mrs C   *She is the Vicar's wife. My sister's Vicar's wife runs the Mothers' Union.*

Madge   *Really. Well, we are not the Mothers' Union and she is not a suitable person, Vicar's wife or not.*

Mrs C   *Yes, well there wasn't much else I could do after Mrs Fillibert let us down. I said it was food poisoning. I didn't say anything about, you know, that dreadful man and her husband and the garden hoe.*

Madge   *I expect she'll find out about that and ring the tabloid press. They seem to know everything else going on here.*

Mrs C   *Oh no, I should think . . . oh you will have your little joke, Madge. Anyway she'll only come to one. I've asked her to keep it light.*

Madge   *Not difficult, I should say. She always seems to be grinning like a Cheshire cat at the most unsuitable times. Well, I'm sorry to say I shall not be coming and shall not send my apologies.*

Mrs C   *Madge, no. Please, I mean . . . look, I'll go round and have a word. A strong word, Madge. Madge . . . oh dear.*

May 6 Wednesday

Mrs Cottee's rage matched her red hair. She swept through our front door, unasked, holding up magazine like a dead rat and demanding who was responsible for 'this outrage.' My tea and soothing noises bulldozed aside. She read out the four lines I'd put in (Women's Hour. Speaker: Vicar's Wife. 17, Back Lane, 7.30pm. Wednesday May 13) 'Shall be writing to the Bishop,' she finished. We stood glaring at each other. John came in. Could he go and play with Simon. He'd lost his watch after games. I interrogated him about what he'd done to find it (nothing of course). Mrs Cottee stalked out, slamming door. Roared off in car. Dreadful grating, crunching sound. Deathly silence. John said he might have left watch in showers. Colin brought in Mrs C in state of shock. John ran off. Mrs C apparently misjudged angle of gate, tore off car bumper just as Colin arrived. I made tea. Found biscuits in back of cupboard, removed mouldy ones. Mrs C terrified of telling Mr C (quiet soul, becomes wild beast when protecting car). What could she tell   him? I sent Colin out, puzzled but relieved not to have to cope. Mrs C grovelled and I agreed to her story. Visit to me, magazine row, door slamming blotted from history.

Anonymous driver in Range Rover ripped off bumper by reversing into her and sped off. Vicar's wife saw it all – good witness. I promised to grease John's palm with silver to forget having seen her in our house (I didn't say he didn't notice she was there – too great an humiliation for her after such an afternoon). Told Colin Mrs C didn't want to have accident mentioned to her husband – he didn't inquire further.

CHAPTER SEVEN

PUDDING AND PIES

May 7 Thursday

Mother-in-law coming next Monday. Everyone glad. Cleared from second spare room (Judith's got first) derelict dolls house, bent train sets, two boxes of old toys. Found Christian Aid box of tricks under bed.

Mrs Cottee rang. Husband 'not pleased' at accident but blaming Range Rover driver.

May 8 Friday

Took Christian Aid stuff round to Bessants. Meekly bore his lecture on leaving it all too late. 'Forward planning, that's the key. No army ever won a battle without a plan of campaign.' He's made up for my neglect with pep talks to the 'troops'. Joyce asked, rather sarcastically, at choir practice if it was alright for her to break the rules and knock three times on doors for envelopes if she knew occupiers were too rheumatic to get to the door quickly. Bessant says twice is 'sufficient to ascertain that the party has temporarily vacated the premises.' And what about the hard of hearing? I quoted herself at herself – her idea to give 'naughty children' a job to do. Bessant one of the naughtiest I know. Deathly silence from her – then ghost of a smile.

May 9 Saturday

Dennis rang to say he'd bring round two barbecues ready for evening. I said 'humbugs'. He chortled. I know he knew I'd forgotten youth barbecue in our garden. Told him to put them off and I'd get the food in. Didn't tell him last year a parish barbecue ended in fire destroying 20 yards of farmer's hedge. Judith said could she invite 'a few friends.' Later she started fire with no problem. Lesley helped in kitchen, set fire to oven gloves. Clare doused her with greasy contents of washing up bowl, ruined new gear. Screamed at each other. Judith lent her a top and skirt. Bernard turned up at Judith's invitation. Didn't go to youth seminar. Parish business he said. Oh dear. Stephanie will not be pleased. Judith and friends very good – didn't produce wine until youth group went. Re-started party and barbecue. All except Judith got distinctly merry and all left vintage cars in our drive when she drove them home.

Anne, John and Colin ('some of us have got our busiest day tomorrow') went to bed about 10pm. I cleared lawn of charcoal, litter and Bernard (fast asleep under hedge). Judith dragged him into our wheelbarrow, trundled him inside, tipped him on sofa. Colin asleep, couldn't tell him.

May 10 Sunday

Overslept. Didn't hear Colin get up for 8am service, discover Bernard stumbling about downstairs trying to find loo. Bernard gone when I got down. Colin gave brief, chilly outline of scene. He couldn't get car out round vintage cars so had to ride my bike in his cassock. Stephanie not in church. She pushed note under our door.

Note From Stephanie

Shall not be in Church this am. Think youth work thing was mentally and physically and spiritually exhausting, besides being totally unsuitable for our parish. Other people from similar parishes near us obviously agreed as they didn't attend. I really don't think I'm suited to youth work. Probably better to involve people who do not have a demanding full time job. Everyone else brought sandwiches and enjoyed fellowship during lunch hour but did not extend it to me – fellowship or sandwiches. I feel I should re-examine my whole position in the Church. I expect I'll come to Evensong.

May 11 Monday

Mother-in-law arrived safely. I did easiest part of Christian Aid stint – popping in envelopes and running before irate people start in pursuit. One caught me. Sharp faced woman opened window and shouted she never gave to anything because we're all crooks feathering our own nests and encouraging idleness, irresponsible child bearing and Communism. Thanked her for frank expression of views. Said that was better than people handing back envelopes with nothing in them or saying they'd given already to some other collector. Mrs sour-face shocked. Sorry for me, asked me in to tea. Put £5 in envelope 'but don't think I'll do it every time.' Assured her I'd never take her good nature for granted.

Bouquet arrived from Bernard with card 'with thanks and abject apologies to you all' (his underlining). Probably Stephanie's case is hopeless, but I put flowers in with mother-in-law and didn't show them or card to Judith.

Made cakes for tomorrow's event including cake I'm to decorate in shape of our Church. I hope.

May 12 Tuesday

Pleased with cake. Stayed up till midnight on it but dropped it on our drive on way to sale. Retrieved nave and chancel, tried to remould as country cottage. Failed. Made boring sponge instead. Lisa's mother brought along three fantastic gateaux. Sold within three minutes. Mine didn't. Sale made £63.

May 13 Wednesday

Couldn't put it off any longer. Went round collecting envelopes. Quite pleasant. Mrs Briggs said she thought people putting into Church collection should be exempt from giving (crosses on front doors perhaps). That recluse still shut in house since brother's death. Shouted through letter box she had secret ways of stopping KGB from dragging her before firing squad. Told Colin. He said he and doctor 'have the situation in hand.' Opened envelopes. £22.5p from two roads.

Did a Trivia Quiz at Women's Hour. Amazed to see who belongs to this shady group. Mrs Fearns, for instance, and the two Miss Wallaces, who told me how to make jelly bags from old tights (can't say I fancy it). Mrs Cottee welcomed me to the 'select gathering.' Not asked to join. Or told when and where next meeting is.

May 14 Thursday

Told Doris at shop about meeting. Surprised I was asked as formed 20 years ago as pressure group to stop certain clergyman chosen by PCC from coming as Vicar. Won battle. Victory went to their heads. Kept up group in case needed again. Didn't campaign against Colin 'so far as she knew.' While waiting for next struggle invited speakers and did craft work. Membership by invitation. Told Colin – not amused. In fact as annoyed as I've seen him for ages – except over Bernard on Sunday of course.

May 15 Friday

Christian Aid envelopes coming in slowly. Twisted Derek's arm at choir practice to operate dreaded harmonium for Rogation next week. Didn't tell Joyce about it.

May 16 Saturday

Bernard's parish rang to say could we give them more Christian Aid envelopes as they'd expanded their operation. Told them I'd not a single one left in the house – true. Ours all with Bessant.

May 17 Sunday

Stephanie still a little cold with me. Told her there was a good story about fantastic increase in Christian Aid giving in Bernard's parish. (What's the matter with her? If I'd waited for Colin to make the moves I'd still be toiling in an office for my living instead of living a life of luxury in Vicarage).

May 18 Monday

Rest of envelopes came in £1304 altogether, £20 down on last year. Heard Bernard's parish raised £2600 (Thou shalt not covet thy neighbour's millionaire residents and pushy collectors).

May 19 Tuesday

Dennis called to say Youth Group walk Saturday postponed but, before I got too excited, told me a group he knew from up north somewhere would be camping locally over weekend. Wants our lot to join them Saturday evening for a do. Camping! I hope their enthusiasm for creepy crawly life under canvas doesn't wear off on ours.

May 20 Wednesday

Clergy Wives meeting. All enthusiastic about session in autumn on Dealing With Stress. I said I'd been too stressed over parish to read literature we'd had about it. Some of us, said Sally Jeffries, had husbands with several parishes, children still at playschool and awkward PCCs and churchwardens and all without help from newly retired people. I said I was sure the event would be 'helpful' and let them put my name down. I'm bound to be treble booked on that day – I am most days – so should get out of it. Elsie there, look surprised I was so grumpy with them. Doesn't realise clergy wives en masse always bring out the worst in me. I don't mind some of them individually. Elsie said, privately, perhaps I'd forgotten how tiring and stressful small children could be. Colin lucky to have one parish. I said very true but didn't see why I had to soak up their stress. She said: 'Why not?' For such a nice person she packs quite a punch.

Judith introduced us to plain looking young man called Hank with an Austin 7 she described as 'beautiful' – think she meant both car and man. She chugged off with both of them.

May 21 Thursday

Felt so guilty at total neglect of mother-in-law spent day with her at semi-stately home and garden. Colin over-worked she thinks – children doing well – my position that of unpaid Curate.

Arthur managed panic note after I'd only been away a day. Sam Thompson can't lend us his farm trailer for harmonium's visit to fields on Sunday for Rogation. What was I going to do about it? Leave Sam's crops unblessed for a start was my first reaction. The second was that I'm an unpaid Curate so must do something about it. Decided to ask scouts for help.

May 22 Friday

Scouts willing to do their duty and lend us their trailer Sunday. Haven't told Derek his perch will be even more unsafe than usual on these outings. Produce Association dinner at Red Lion tonight. Read all about it in newspaper, then remembered having heard about Bessant's part in it.

Report In Local Newspaper

Feuding villagers are fighting it out not on the beaches but on the dinner tables and it looks like being a case of puddings at dawn. Traditionalists at the village Produce Association are demanding a return to stodgy puddings and Real Ale at the annual dinner after years of what they call 'rabbit food' – a salad buffet.

Landlord Donald Davis says he is quite willing to provide anything his customers want but it's true his wife would love to return to her speciality, steak and kidney pudding.

Her skill had been overlooked until she was asked about it by leader of the traditionalists, Mr S Bessant, who told your reporter: 'It is the duty of us country folk to show the rest of the country what it means to return to the old ways and customs. This country became great on a diet of suet puddings.'

Speaker at this year's dinner is the Vicar, who earlier this year was at the centre of several other rows in this far from peaceful village. He was unavailable for comment. A parishioner said she understood his favourite meal was egg and chips followed by lemon meringue pie with cream.

Colin and I clobbered by both sides. Salad group sat with buffet in one room, suet puds had long table in other. Both recruiting from 'don't knows'. Fred Padget, handyman and only parishioner ever known to help in our garden, was pud man but Mr Wilson, whose wife and daughter still need kid glove treatment, booked by his wife into salads. So it went on. Allies of ours on both sides. What to do? Landlord solved it. Put up small table for the two of us in doorway. Suggested we grab some salad from buffet and hot food from passing staff. We managed – just. Puds drank more ale. Noisier, dirtier jokes. Salads drank dry white wine, settled business of year among them. Colin called on them in speech not to turn gastronomic dispute into 100 years war with everyone forgetting what started it.

May 23 Saturday

Very muddy everywhere. Exceptionally muddy on camp site with visiting Youth Group and ours. They didn't mind. Played rounders. Ours a bit alarmed at guitar playing, hymn singing afterwards round camp fire but almost got over embarrassment before end. Tamar and visiting youth seem to have formed lasting passion. Surprising as he was in charge of hymn singing and she's, well, not very devout. On way home she said perhaps she'd go in for Voluntary Service Overseas, like whatshisname, the new boyfriend, when she left school. But not to tell her parents. No danger. They'll blame me for such a bizarre idea and expect me to talk her back into teaching or bank clerking.

Dennis said perhaps the mud will have cleared by tomorrow? Oh no! Rogation.

May 24 Sunday

Still drizzling. Colin announced Rogation Service would go ahead as per tradition. Colin and I loaded harmonium from hall on to scout trailer. Handful of people turned up. Choir wore wellingtons and lots of clothes. Derek refused to operate harmonium while perched precariously on wonky trailer. Joyce said he was right. Foolish custom. Better go inside and bless things from there. Prayers just as efficacious indoors as out. So we blessed stream, field, gardens etc inside. Disappointing not to have cries, jeers and unexpected joining in of hymns from passers by. Not like last year when we sang on boundary during a cricket match and umpire couldn't decide whether it was a boundary when the ball dropped into the top of the harmonium.

May 25 Monday

Colin persuaded to go out for day with his mother, me and kids (half term). Discarded his dog collar even. Went to coast. Judith away for school holiday. Young man, Hank, keeps ringing and won't believe she's just not here. What is that relationship all about?

May 26 Tuesday

Couldn't lure Colin out for second day. Children, mother-in-law and I went out. Took children to cinema while she went round shops and a museum. John said film rubbish but the museum really interesting. Anne said film rubbish and she really needed new clothes.

May 27 Wednesday

Children's friends round most of day. Ben, kid John and Anne both say they can't make out, don't like and didn't ask to come, tagged along and then vanished. I found him in John's room sitting by flickering fire in grate – probably its first for 30 years. Called children and asked them to play with him, please. Put fire out, phoned his mother. 'He's going through a phase,' she said. 'He's fascinated by fire. I thought there was a box of matches missing from the kitchen.' Returned Ben and matches later. Anne says he lit a fire in a bush near school playing field last week.

May 28 Ascension Day

Killed the old tradition of meeting to sing hymns at 5.30am some years ago on understanding that I cooked everyone breakfast in the house after service at a more reasonable hour. About 20 came. I ate my only cooked breakfast of the year and as usual felt ill all day. Everyone else said it was great, so it can't be the food.

John says can he have a fire in his room every day when it's cold.

May 29 Friday

People at choir practice speculating on whether indoor blessing of gardens would work as well as outdoor reminded me it's time for my annual venture into horticulture because (a) everything's grown enough for me to tell what's a weed; (b) It'll be hard enough work to make me feel I've done enough to last a long time; (c) Stanley's coming tomorrow on PCC business and will tell everyone I've turned over a new leaf; (d) mother-in-law still here and is bound to help and she knows what she's doing.

May 30 Saturday

Mother-in-law spent day with friend not in my garden. Recent rain encouraged weeds to pretend they were Amazonian jungle. Most of proper plants had given up. Colin said he'd have to spend a fortune on bedding plants – whatever they are. And Stanley came in time to see me secretly replanting the one good rose in the rose garden after I'd mistakenly dug it up. Gave me an account of what that bed used to look like 20 years ago. Judith home tonight.

May 31 Sunday

Sunday School mime going well without me. Knocked off and went home for coffee. Judith and Hank shouting at each other in her room. I flushed loo tactfully. Noise stopped.

CHAPTER EIGHT

CAUGHT OUT

June 1 Monday

A young woman ran up drive fairly early this morning in great distress – hair and clothes a mess, panting, sobbing. Only understandable words 'get me,' 'help,' 'Vicar.' Colin just about getting up. Woman refused tea and sympathy or to move from doorstep. Milkman's float arrived, she screamed. Colin came down. Woman (Bridget) flung herself at him (I was unmoved – wives with spouses in other jobs probably thinking of paternity suits by now). She lives on remote farm with husband, no children. Husband turned violent, tried to throw her down a well. Three hours' counselling from Colin then she said she'd venture back home to 'give it another chance' but with Colin in tow. He returned alone pretty soon looking shaken. A large fierce husband had roared at her. Bridget then told him Colin had lured her into religion and 'made suggestions.' It was then Colin's turn for the well. Exit clergyman pursued by giant.

'I shouldn't have left her,' Colin said two hours later. I restrained him from going back. 'But if anything should happen to her I'd never forgive myself' he said. I sent him down to Dennis to talk it over. They decided Colin should leave it a bit then pay a social call with me to calm man's jealousy – or to have someone else for the well.

Mother-in-law left today. I'm not really surprised.

June 2 Tuesday

Colin still worried about Bridget so I mentioned the magic words St James's to take his mind off it. That worked. Now he's worried what we're to do to give the old saint a fitting celebration for his patronal festival next month. Actually I've already decided on something – thought I'd better as last year we forgot all about him and booked holiday for St Jamestide (Cancelled when Arthur looked pained). We'll have disco Friday for energetic, Garden Party Saturday for optimistic, play about St James by Sunday

School and Youth Group and an organ recital. Must contact disco outfit brownies had, arrange to borrow tents for fete refreshments, think of stalls and ask St John's Ambulance to do demonstration as they owe me for work on their Jumble Sale last January. Also write play. I let Colin carry on worrying.

June 3 Wednesday

Told Colin about my plans. Had to because now something else is bugging him. He had discretely planned to whisk Jason Ferns off to obscure parish for Confirmation Thursday. No fuss. Christopher thrilled at having 'fixed him like I said I would.' But Bishop ill, all cancelled.

Rang disco outfit – prices horrendous. Said forget it, we'd organise our own. Told Anne and John this. They said nothing *loudly*. I'll show 'em. Tents for fete OK. Started serious research on St James.

June 4 Thursday

Think I'll ask Judith to do disco. PCC secretary, Nellie, rang to say she's not free on Saturday am after all so could Colin take over. Take over what? I sensed I'd end up doing it whatever it was as Colin's busy.

Colin came in saying police called by Bridget. PC Hunt went and husband accused him of affair with Bridget, ordered him to leave or the dreaded well. I forgot about Nellie's message. Must tell Colin tomorrow. Can't be important, can it?

June 5 Friday

It's Ellery's missionary society coming to see Church to decide whether to install lights as a memorial to him and what sort of plaque they want. And I was right. I'm taking them round as I'm unbiased in stained glass row ie no one on PCC has time or inclination. Colin thinks he invited them to lunch but can't be sure. I'll get a salad instead of usual Saturday egg, chips and sausages. More fitting for missionaries somehow.

Stephanie still moping, but I've got an idea. Spring has got to Joyce. Turned up to practice in prettyish dress and *with her hair different* – softer round face. Perhaps she fancies Bernard as well.

Letter From Missionary Society

We note with appreciation your suggestion that a memorial to one of our late members should go up in your Church. We are greatly encouraged to know that our work in the mission field has come to your attention and after much discussion have decided that providing this memorial will give great impetus to our publicity and fund raising activities in your parish. The appropriate department will be pleased to provide you with a comprehensive standing display and collecting boxes and we hope it will prove possible for you to appoint an honorary organiser locally.

We were especially grateful for your letter as we had not previously been aware of the very great contribution Mr Ellery made to our society in its early years. He seems to have been one of that noble army of servants of God content to 'hide their light under a bushel.' But extensive research has uncovered a few valuable facts about his life. The exact nature of his connection with your parish is not immediately obvious, making it difficult for us to suggest wording for a plaque, but no doubt you will be able to elucidate for us.

My colleague and I plan to visit your Church on June 6 for further discussions with, we hope, the full PCC and we look forward to a continuing association with you begun by that notable son of the parish, Ellery.

June 6 Saturday

Mission people were a sensible, middle aged clergyman and friendly woman of about 28 just back from somewhere outlandish that makes you feel guilty about confining Christian activity to places with running water and proper roads. Seemed a bit vague about Ellery. Offered to leave publicity material with us. Think we'll probably end up giving them more than it costs them for the lights. Didn't stay to lunch. Colin, John and Anne bought fish and chips. Judith and I ate salad.

June 7 Sunday

Sunday School effort went well. Only mistakes from tots and the more they got it wrong and looked round for mum the more the congregation liked it.

June 8 Monday

Geoffrey rang while Colin was out to ask if he'd turn out for clergy in charity cricket match next Saturday. At least that's what I thought he said in his vague way as he was mainly apologising for last minute appeal. Colin over the moon, although trying to be modest and rate his claims as all rounder below those of an England player. Rang round sportsmen in our congregation for gear (his last bat and pads will soon fit John). Geoffrey rang again, Colin answered and learned, half way through the conversation, they actually need him as umpire. I realised something was wrong and blame was getting round to me so went out to visit the sick until the worse passed over. Three hours later he was past anger and into resigned depression at advancing years. At tea he said the team was 'made up of raw youngsters like Bernard.' Judith said she liked cricket and would probably go along to cheer Bernard. I rang Stephanie to suggest she orders a photographer and comes along to report.

June 9 Tuesday

Colin got his own back on me. Threw me a note at breakfast from Bishop's secretary reminding him his lordship's dropping in on us on Friday afternoon as arranged. He'd forgotten to tell me but I couldn't rant and rave after cricket mistake. De-junking session everywhere. No quarter given. All rooms and contents, including study, subjected to black rubbish bag treatment from tomorrow morning. Fantastic activity all evening even from Judith, although I said visitor's bedroom not a legitimate place for Bishops to be. (Last time I de-junked Colin lost a year's worth of sermons, one cufflink and broken 21st birthday travelling clock; Anne a tape; John a pair of trainers and shorts; cat three table tennis balls and dead mouse stored behind dresser as a midnight snack). All rooms eventually looked beautifully tidy. Then I said de-junking would include under beds. More frantic activity. And I said, removal of anything falling out of cupboards when opened. Finally finished. Anne said did rules apply to me as a load of photo albums had fallen out of landing cupboard when opened. I gathered them up with dignity and put them in a box for taking to the loft with the other 15 boxes the rest of them had put out for storage.

June 10 Wednesday

Colin and I drove with shaking limbs to Bridget's homestead, half expecting shotguns at the windows. Everything quiet and empty looking. Colin said he hoped they'd not moved before he had a chance for a 'proper talk.' I said I hoped they'd moved, preferably to Johnson's parish. I notice Colin only knocked very gently and quickly decided they were out and walked back to the car. Mr Bridget (don't know name) arrived from somewhere. Colin assumed pastoral visiting look, offered his hand. 'Yes?' barked Mr Bridget. Colin said he'd come with Church magazine. The man made us understand he was unlikely to be interested in the Men's Fellowship talk by Arthur on Travels In The Holy Land (with colour slides) or even the outing (wives welcome) to the theatre. I mumbled something about Mothers and Toddlers. That's when he raised an arm, complete with evil looking spanner. We backed to car and escaped. Colin felt he could have done better.

Sent Colin down to pub to play fruit machines and mingle socially. Came back with full story from PC Hunt. Bridget and man not married. He left wife and three kids to run off with Bridget. Dotes on her. She taunts him with stories of affairs with other men. When Colin told PC Hunt I'd mentioned Mothers and Toddlers he was surprised we'd escaped with our lives as Mr Bridget (I think it's Hobson) keeps trying to snatch his kids from his wife.

Didn't get any de-junking done but cast Hoover over sitting room and changed towel in downstairs loo. Then remembered loo probably wouldn't work, even for Bishop, so put clean towel upstairs. Realised I'd have to tidy that loo as well.

June 11 Thursday

Spent *all day* cleaning. If only I did some every day – or even every week – these emergencies wouldn't happen. (Yes they would. Housework never stays done). Colin hoped I'd hadn't thrown out his official returns for registrar – three weeks late already. I said not if they were in filing cabinet under Registrar – Official Returns but probably yes if they were still on the dresser. He slammed into study and I rushed outside, searched contents of dustbin, found returns in envelope near bottom (only slightly smeared with ketchup), put it prominently on dresser. Colin found it there at tea time. Suitably cowed. I didn't lie. I didn't say I hadn't thrown it away.

June 12 Friday

At least the house is clean. I needn't do much for ages. Bishop only stayed 20 minutes and didn't look under beds or even admire completely clear draining boards. Shining silver teapot unused. I like him. Has a poetic turn of phrase and unworldly approach to life. He had to rush off to another appointment. Hoped he hadn't put me to any trouble. Of course not, I said. When he'd gone Colin started desperate search. Bishop's last words were 'Look forward to seeing you both next month.' That reminded Colin he'd lost invite to Bishop's Garden Party. Said he'd have to ask discreetly round the deanery.

June 13 Saturday

Fine drizzle this morning. Colin trying to feel sorry for fate of cricket match when he felt it served them right for discarding him. (Wonder if Test Match players feel same when they're 12th man and it rains – at least they don't have failure rubbed in by having to umpire). It brightened up mid morning, just right for match on bumpy field in Geoffrey's parish. Visitors won cricket match by 40 runs, most of our players blaming Colin for his decisions, and Judith won battle for Bernard's attention by doing the scoring. Stephanie's photographer didn't show up. She really didn't have to apologise for having to publish Bernard's duck when he and Judith treated the whole thing as a huge joke.

Geoffrey's wife organised impressive refreshments – sort of efficiency I find very stressful. Judith invited Bernard out to some event of car crowd. I was so nearly sure I surprised a look of triumph towards Stephanie, who chugged off alone on moped I told Hank when he phoned that Judith had 'vanished into the distance with one of our clerical cricketers.' He slammed the phone down.

Colin's discovered the Bishop's GP is July 9.

June 14 Sunday

Barry was bleeped to a fire call during Communion. All the choir round him changed notes to bleeper tone. He left but came back to satisfy our curiosity. Chimney fire, no one hurt. Colin went round to see if he could help and unearthed problems ranging from teenage son's girlfriend's treachery to loss of husband's earnings through drink driving offence.

June 15 Monday

Bernard came round. He's supposed to organise parish country dancing on his lawn after immemorial custom (or since wife of previous Vicar thought of it). Hasn't a clue – and it's next week. Help! I got half way through list – order band, print tickets, posters, food, pretend he'd had it in hand for weeks – when thought of Stephanie. Told him she was a whiz at organising such things. That'll throw them together and let her find out if she really wants to be a Vicar's wife and spend lifetime doing that. She rang to say a 'miracle' had happened. Bernard was beginning to turn to her. Did I want tickets for a country dance next week? Oh – and did I know how to organise band, tickets etc. Put her on to our Folk Dance Group.

June 16 Tuesday

Stephanie rang four times with queries. Just as well Bernard's busy as Hank turned up. Rest of us closed our ears to row in Judith's room. Hank stormed downstairs, slammed out of front door breaking one of little stained glass panes.

June 17 Wednesday

Sewing Meeting ladies had brilliant idea to keep me occupied while listening to gossip – patchwork. Not a quilt of my own, of course, but helping the Miss Wallaces with theirs by cutting bits of paper and pinning material to them. No sewing.

June 18 Thursday

Elsie worried about grandchild in hospital, going to Shropshire to visit. Dennis sorry but must miss Youth Group. Then man from council rang to say German teenagers and pastor visiting area and he'd told them to contact me to find something for them to do on Saturday as he didn't work weekends. Thanks, he said, before I could think of anything to say. Rang off. No details. German pastor rang to thank us for hospitality but how was he to get to us from four miles out in the country. Told him I'd be in touch. Too late to do anything today.

June 19 Friday

Decided both German and our kids might as well all come here. All morning cooking, ringing our Youth Group mums for refreshments. Most alright. One said she thought the Church 'should do that sort of thing.' Still no transport arranged. Told Joyce about it at choir practice. She knows the very youth officer who landed us in this bother and exclaimed 'typical' before telling me to tell the pastor they'd be picked up at 6pm. I asked no questions.

June 20 Saturday

Put food out and trusted in Providence and Joyce. Germans arrived in mini bus driven by Derek! 'Joyce was desperate for a driver. She got her college mini bus,' he said. Joyce? Desperate? No time to mull that over. Sixteen large German kids, half each boys and girls, plus three guitars in our dining room. Our YG already there. Neither spoke other's language. Total silence. I fluttered about uttering only German I recalled from O level. 'Gutten Tag,' 'Was ist das?' One lad began playing guitar. I suddenly remembered pastor. Poor man standing in hall looking lost but vaguely smiling. His English not too bad so he, Derek and I went into sitting room and forgot kids. Two hours later guitar playing still going on above chatter in some sort of shared language. Two groups finally prized apart amid much promising to write and 'Guten Abend' all round – including from me to pastor as I'd just remembered that phrase too.

2am woke up when motor bike roared past and stayed awake half an hour wondering about Joyce being 'desperate' about something. Derek must have got it wrong. She probably said I was desperately useless.

June 21 Sunday

Stephanie so into Folk Dancing at Bernard's parish she tried to sell Colin and I tickets – last time I did folk dancing was May Pole competition at primary school and was sent to Coventry by whole team for getting tied up in ribbons. Colin has never danced any sort of step ever.

PC Hunt waiting for Colin at Vicarage (forgot we'd be at Church on a Sunday). Bridget's lover – man who threatens people with death down a well you remember, diary – is up in court tomorrow for threatening behaviour to electricity meter man when he called. Bridget's flung him out so wants to stay with us tonight rather than a police cell as Colin's 'the only friend I have in the world.' Colin looked at me quizzically. I opened my mouth to object but the words wouldn't come out so I nodded weakly. But I arranged for kids to stay with friends overnight. Mr Bridget (Theo) spent most of day in study with Colin crying. I fed him. Obviously my Christian duty to have him here – but that doesn't mean I slept peacefully in my bed.

Dennis and Elsie back – grandchild's appendicitis a false alarm.

June 22 Monday

Colin took Theo to court and Theo jailed for six months. Tearful reunion with Bridget at court before being led away. Most of village thinks we harboured a murderer, thanks to Anne and John. I told Doris the truth – just hope it gets round as fast as the other version.

June 23 Tuesday

Met another strange man in the garden when I got home from dentist (trouble ahead if I keep getting up too late to floss). Recognised him as quiet rather sad old bachelor from flat over the supermarket. Always wears a hat and raises it when greeting females. I know, I know – it's not PC but I like it. His ancient dog had died and Colin told him he could bury it in our garden. Nice to have been told earlier so I could have left the man alone to grieve instead of having to ask if Colin had hired him to do the garden. Grave marked with wooden cross. Later Colin said he made the offer six months ago when talking to the man and hadn't realised the dog had died. Was I saying I minded burial in our garden? I didn't. It's live dogs I can't stand.

June 24 Wednesday

This is getting ridiculous. Yet another strange man lurking about when Colin and I got back from school swimming gala (John first in breast stroke) – only he wasn't really strange. It was Mike from Colin's theological college on holiday down this way and dropping in for a chat. He's got a rough and tumble parish in Inner London. Burgled so many times his house is like Fort Knox. 'And how's . . .?' I began when we got inside. 'Put the kettle on,' Colin said, abruptly I thought but I realised they probably wanted to swap tales of croquet matches at dawn and lectures on Old Testament prophets. Made tea for them and children. Found he'd gone. Apparently his wife and three children have given up on the struggle and left, which he'd told Colin in a letter that had not got to me, and wanted to ask his advice on what to do. Stay and minister to the burglars and muggers or find a quiet country parish, such as this one, and minister to his family. Colin a bit evasive about what he said but I strongly suspect that a straight swap could have crossed his mind. At least Mike's parish would be unlikely to have garden fetes and folk dancing and Theo's offences would fade into insignificance. Probably only a thought so no point in putting my oar in – yet.

CHAPTER NINE

MIXED RECEPTIONS

June 25 Thursday

Just as you thought Jane Austen and her ilk were dead we piled into our time machine and transported ourselves to the Big House for an Evening With the Lady Of The Manor, Mrs Delaware. Sudden impulse by Mrs D (widowed with grown up children only seldom down) to invite the professional classes in the village to wine (cheap and nasty) and cheese (ditto). I'm not sure we acquitted ourselves quite to the manor born. Anne put a glass of lemonade (cheap and gassy) on the grand piano leaving a mark, which I covered up with a sheet of music, and I trod crisps (supermarket own brand) into the carpet. John accidentally kicked the leg of a chair and received a lecture from Mrs D on How To Care For Your Chippendales. I offered to do the washing up as a reflex action from countless parish events. 'My dear, we may live in unsettling times but I don't think we need ask the parson's wife to do the household chores,' she said. (I may need that quote often, diary, so keep it safe).

Mrs D cornered Colin for much of evening pouring out the story of errant son lost in a Peruvian jungle with an unsuitable female. 'I'm her Parish Priest as much as anyone else,' he said when we got home. 'She has human needs the same as everyone else.' Human needs, yes, but not like anyone else's, I pointed out.

June 26 Friday

There's no end to the perks of Colin's job it seems. Mrs Delaware summoned her private Chaplain (Colin) to her. Offered to pay for him to go to Peru to find her son and bring him back. 'When do you leave?' I said. 'I tactfully declined,' he said. 'But I don't think I convinced her.'

June 27 Saturday

Back to more or less normal life, or as normal as it gets with Stephanie and the Folk Dancing. It seems she forgot to organise any chairs for exhausted dancers and Bernard's hall committee refused to allow their posh new stacking seating outside for a rowdy event like a folk dance. She tried Leonard in the understandable belief that our chairs were so grotty it wouldn't matter where they went. He swore at her, she said, and put her on to Bessant, who told her to put in an application for loan of chairs and he would consider it in due course. So the only seating they had were Bernard's from the house. There was no band as it got the date wrong and someone had to lend her some tapes. 'I expect they enjoyed it – people usually forget the disasters if they have a good time,' I said when the story was poured out to me over the phone at 2.30am. 'I should know. Disasters always happen around me.' Apparently everyone told her 'never again' – including Bernard.

June 28 Sunday

Persuaded three keen folk dancers in our congregation who were at Bernard's yesterday to tell Stephanie it was the greatest event since that 1960s hippie thing that type is always on about. They mumbled and moaned. One said even I could have staged it better. But they managed to say something encouraging to her so she brightened up a bit. Bernard rang to apologise for upsetting our hall staff. I got him into guilt mode over having put too much of a burden on a girl who was not even in his congregation and he said he'd be sure to tell her of is appreciation.

June 29 Monday

Colin up at Manor House again for even worse news. Son has been in contact with his mother to say he has become a Roman Catholic in sympathy with That Woman and so that he can marry her. Colin's task now is to find him, detach from unsuitable female and Roman Church and bring him back. There seemed no way of getting his refusal through to Mrs Delaware so he's allegedly thinking it over.

June 30 Tuesday

Colin's big chance gone it seems. Bernard rang to say did he know a woman called Delaware from our parish who had phoned to ask him to go to South America on what seemed to be a diplomatic mission because her own private Chaplain had family commitments preventing him from going. Was she eccentric? I took the call and so answered yes to both questions and advised him to mind the Chippendales when he went up to see her to collect his tickets. That'll teach him not to fancy the wife I'd got lined up for him.

July 1 Wednesday

Irate Mrs Wilson dropped in on Mothers and Toddlers. Pamela's back at work, mum babysitting. Colin's told her ten times he'll pop in Baptism form and she's still waiting. Not ten times surely, I said. (It's probably nearer twenty but that made her revise downwards). Told her I'd rush home for a form. None to be found in filing cabinet under Baptism. Typed one from memory, told her it was a new sort we were trying out. Told off Colin. He said he'd been waiting for family situation to calm down and seemed to think the forms were filed under family insurances. (Ours for this life or babies' for the next? I didn't ask).

July 2 Thursday

Helen from Sunday School called about costumes for St James play. Dug out mound of assorted Nativity and panto gear from understairs cupboard. Found five all purpose Bible Lands nightshirts, six pairs wings, two royal cloaks, three female costumes (long). Who do we know that can sew? Loads of people in Sewing Group. Rang round. Some got very excited and promised to run up a selection. I told Colin we'd thought of a way of involving the Church in the School. Thinking of publicity for it reminded me – the magazine!

July 3 Friday

Magazine typing. End result looks like I typed it at 2am.

Miss Wallaces rang to say did we want them to make donkey hobby horse for Sunday School play. They did one once 30 years ago and wanted to try again. Sounds odd, but I can always lose Christopher in it and tell him to keep pawing the ground. He hates having to learn lines but his mum always wants him to be in things.

Noticed letters GP in pencil on kitchen calendar for next Wednesday (must be important. Don't usually remember to write anything on it except 'take bread out of freezer' or 'it's now too late to send Aunt Emma a card because her birthday was last month'). Woke up at 2.35am and remembered GP meant Bishop's Garden Party – woke Colin to tell him. He thought event next Wednesday not urgent enough for such a drastic measure.

Dennis rang to say 12 going canoeing, can I take some in car? – alright, but I'm definitely not taking to the water. He assured me I could drop them off, go back home and come back to fetch them. Definitely unwatery. Derek and Joyce working on organ recital. He's allowed one in every three pieces in 'lighter vein,' Joyce said. Pamela's unfortunate baby to receive its diabolical name on Sunday.

July 4 Saturday

Mix up over transport to canoeing. Dennis got his lot there but I got lost. When I found the right bit of water no time to go back so stayed. Lured into canoe – slipped getting out and sat in water. All laughed. Everyone enjoyed whole thing, except me. (Yes I did, in retrospect. Anne and John thought I was 'very brave' to have ventured. And stupid).

July 5 Sunday

Sewing meeting ladies churning out costumes like sweat shop workers. Donkey costume's 'taking shape' the Miss Wallaces told Colin. What shape though? Pamela's baby finally Baptised.

Magazine had 24 spelling mistakes, the sidesmen's rota was for the wrong month and the centre pages were in upside down. Arthur said what we needed was an editor who 'had more time' and had I met a middle aged couple who'd sat at the back for a few weeks. He introduced me (as Vicar's wife, not named person – grrr) to Jill and Steve Medlicott 'who say they know a thing or two about parish magazines' and then left us. 'He's lying,' said Jill bluntly in an accent from up north somewhere. 'What I said was your magazine has the same problems as our old one.' I bravely asked what those were and she said 'Apathy. No one wants to contribute or help, everyone wants it in their hands on time.' Steve hastily added that our magazine cover was very attractive, but I said 'I suppose you wouldn't like to take it over?' 'Yes, alright,' she said. 'I shall step on toes but you won't mind that?' Of course I said that was quite alright. Told Colin of the new volunteer. 'Well I hope we won't regret it,' Colin said, 'Like the Bessants.'

July 6 Monday

Jill came round first thing – that is my period of getting round to doing something after the children have gone to school – to discuss the magazine. 'No getting me to do other Church jobs,' she said. 'I know you Vicar's wives pounce on willing newcomers.' I would have denied such an allegation but then I'd not be able to ask her to help with coffee and Youth Group, serve on school governors or infiltrate Women's Group at a later state. She left with threat to leave out Vicar's letter if it's ever late. Good luck to her, I say. 'You'll regret it,' Colin said. He might, I won't.

Brownie lady met me in street and asked if they could use our front lawn for sports day. I said yes but calling it a lawn was an exaggeration. She looked and said could her husband come round and 'get things ready.' And perhaps I wouldn't mind if he brought their new mower. They could bring a combine harvester and it wouldn't make any difference, I thought, but bowed before such hearty enthusiasm for outdoor group activities.

Asked Judith if St James disco was in hand. It is. Apparently Hank's working on it and it involves lots of sessions up in her room and going down to the hall together to investigate. This could be good news for Stephanie, but she's hardly spoken to me since the folk dancing and her moped's so seriously broken she's using her brother's old bicycle and is slowly sinking into resigned spinsterhood – at 22.

Searched wardrobe for gear to wear at Bishop's Garden Party. Best summer dress alright but cat's used my ordination straw hat for a bed. Judith offered to lend me hers. But she, Anne and John laughed so much at Judith's large hat on my head, I decided to go hatless. Anne said if I went in my old flat shoes she'd leave home. John said why did going to such a friendly chap's party involve such a lot of fuss. If he was going he'd wear his jeans, denim jacket and second best trainers. Good idea, I thought. But his second best trainers won't fit me.

July 7 Tuesday

Beautiful sunny day – pity it turned into such a fiasco. Colin and I planned to make a day of it, go early and eat a pub lunch (Diocesan teas always rely on tiny square sandwiches and tired quiches turning into enough to feed hundreds and they never do). This great scheme failed as Colin just 'nipped round to open up the Church.' Met Stanley, stayed two hours inspecting the grass in the gutters and deciding whether to ask expensive professional or dangerous amateur – I didn't ask what they decided. I didn't want to know. No time for any sort of lunch. Made it to the Palace just in time. Palace lawn empty so made for refreshments in giant marquee. Place full of immensely grand African couples eating fabulous food. Not a weedy Vicar, scruffy wife or curled sandwich in sight.

They looked at us and smiled. Smart waitress almost offered us food but walked off. We turned to escape. My heels stuck and I fell to my knees just as our Bishop entered. 'Please don't kneel, it's only me,' he said. 'The food's better than usual, do have some.' Colin dragged me up and mumbled something about the wrong day. 'I know, I know,' said the Bishop. 'But you'll enjoy this much more – and you can always come back tomorrow.' We even had wine after the Bishop had introduced us as 'all part of my splendid team.' Quite a few chatted to us politely about how they were learning such a lot from their whistle stop tour of the Diocese and had brought warm greetings from their congregations. And if we were ever in Zambia we were to pop in.

Anne was surprised I hadn't died of embarrassment (so was I). John said could he go and play cricket and Judith laughed so much she forgot to tell us until several hours later that Arthur had called to say Fred Padget had fallen off a ladder and broken his ankle while inspecting the gutters and what was our position on insurance.

July 8 Wednesday

Yet another Garden Party. Poured with rain. Marquee leaked, 200 clergy and spouses very wet. Back to usual food. No wine. Johnson brought his own hip flask. Geoffrey tried to stop him imbibing but without success. 'Lovely to see you again so soon,' the Bishop said and made several ears prick up. How could those words be translated into prospects for preferment? I heard them thinking. Lashed out yesterday's unspent lunch money on what Colin called the first decent meal he'd had in days. Pie and chips.

Colin visited Fred Padget who kept apologising for being so clumsy and letting the Church down and promising to be up the ladder again and do the job properly as soon as the doc would let him.

July 9 Thursday

Saw Mrs Cottee – Women's Hour boss – asked me to go on their outing to some stately home next Wednesday. Felt pleased to have made this breakthrough.

July 10 Friday

Doris at paper shop said she'd heard so many had cried off the WH outing they were desperate for anyone, even men or Methodists. Also had I asked how much because it was likely 10 people would have to pay for a 45 seater coach. Plus entrance. Plus meals as the WH crowd were not into sandwiches and crisps. I decided not to go. Colin said to make up my own mind but it seemed ideal for 'drawing the group deeper into the fellowship of the Church.' (He wants a spy in the camp since he's not had time to deal with them). Alright. I'll go. But he'll have to pay. Rang Mrs Cottee and she was so delighted I know Doris's version must be true.

July 11 Saturday

Brownie sports OK. Stephanie turned up to report it, found Judith surrounded by admiring circle of assorted children. I had spent morning laying out race track, putting up barbecue etc. while Brown Owl sat in our kitchen and cried about a selection of problems including schoolgirl daughter's pregnancy, son's gambling debts, husband's blaming both on her because of time spent on Brownies and cat run over by lorry.

Colin turned up for last ten minutes of sports to be thanked for kindness and trouble, so I told him about Brown Owl's problem so he can earn the praise. Said he knew about it and it was all exaggerated. (Exaggerated? A pregnancy?)

July 12 Sunday

Could hardly wait through service to ask Doris about exaggerated pregnancy. She said Brown Owl the hysterical type, often cries over newspaper counter. The daughter's just started going out with first boyfriend and mum's imagining the worst. Son was seen once in games arcade. Husband runs the scouts so unlikely to complain about her involvement in youth work. Doris didn't know about cat so I toured council estate asking. Brown Owl's neighbour said it was true.

July 13 Monday

Colin took day off so we spent money on holiday. Decided at 11am to go into town to book something. Colin kept wondering whether he could leave 'his people' safely in hands of Dennis. He knew he could, I knew he could, he knew I knew he could, so I threatened to unfrock him in the street if he didn't go into the travel agent's at once. Booked ten days on a cabin cruiser on a French canal. Neither of us can handle a boat (remember the canoe, diary), there's a day and night travelling across France in a train to get there even if we can find the boat and we shan't dare to let the children up from the cabin but at least *we're on our way.* Anne and John tried to appear blasé but they're thrilled really – aren't they? Judith strangely evasive about whether she'd be home to mind the shop.

July 14 Tuesday

Mrs Cottee rang to confirm I was going on outing. I suggested asking Derby and Joan Club along as special treat for them if she happened to have any spare seats. She almost wept with gratitude (at this rate I shall qualify for membership and have to think of reasons for not going to meetings).

Colin and children asked out for meals tomorrow. Parish obviously thinks I'm a cruel and unfeeling wife and mother to abandon them so. I am, I am. But truly this outing is not one of unashamed luxury and careless abandon.

July 15 Wednesday

As I said, diary, no luxury and careless abandon. Had to sit next to Nelly (PCC secretary). Nice woman but there's one and a half seats worth of her and visibly spreading as she downed crisps, Mars bars, biscuits and fizzy drinks. Heard how she's being hotly pursued by boss at office with offers of overtime and training sessions on computer. Didn't like to say possibly he might be offering overtime and training sessions on computer. Stayed with me all day, demolished vast lunch, two cream teas and several reputations in her office and the village. Oh, I do wish I could believe her version of how Mr Bessant chased her into her own home – 'with-you-know-what in mind,' but there are several witnesses to the loud words they exchanged on that occasion about her not telling him the deanery synod was meeting in the hall and letting him go ahead and arrange a dog show and have to cancel it with much loss of face. But at least with her I avoided walk round stately home gardens and comments about how beautiful Vicarage garden used to be *in the old days*. Nelly and I spent most of day in the downmarket café gently dozing.

Note from Colin when I got back saying would I judge primary school sports Friday. Jill's persuaded Mrs Cottee to write article about outing for magazine. Boring piece but a major breakthrough.

Mrs Cottee's Article In Parish Magazine

The weather was obviously going to be kind to us we realised as we boarded the coach for our visit to the beautiful house and grounds of Col and Mrs Geoffrey de Vere-Hysmith. The journey was uneventful and we arrived in time for morning coffee in a coffee lounge tastefully converted from the old stable block.

Those of us with a feel for the gracious life of times past were treated to a private tour of the house and more secluded parts of the gardens by a member of the staff, which was the highlight of our day.

Those who denied themselves this pleasure certainly missed an experience of considerable cultural significance. The cuisine offered in the more superior of the two restaurants was superb. Our thanks are due to the Family for opening their beautiful home to the discerning public in this way.

CHAPTER TEN

HOME AND DRY

July 16 Thursday

My birthday. Somehow I always expect it'll be a national occasion with me waving to crowds, broadcasting to the nation and attending concert of my favourite music in a dress chain stores rush to copy. None of that happened. Colin said if I liked to choose a dress from the shop in the village he'd pay. Sorry, he'd forgotten a card. Anne and John had made cards and gave me bath cubes. Judith offered to pay for Colin and I to go out to dinner and to child sit. Colin said he'd got a funeral visit to do so perhaps we could go some other time. I stormed out of house followed by Judith and we decided to go to an Indian restaurant in town with her friends, leaving Colin in the drive calling out something about who would child sit. Halfway to the restaurant I got Judith to bring me back. Colin said we'd go out tomorrow.

July 17

Offended practically everyone by insisting on disqualifying the more unpleasant children (mercifully few) who were too competitive and rewarding effort even when, strictly speaking, coming a bad last is not really the same as coming first, second or third – my own childhood experiences at Sports Day coming out here I think as I never even completed a race. The other judges and most of the parents seem to have either had happier times at sports when young or to have forgotten what it feels like to lose your egg in egg and spoon, your sack in the sack race and your way in a bunny hop.

Last day of school term – children's reports good. Headmaster retiring, everyone suddenly saying how wonderful and loved he was. Up to yesterday he was a 'fossil' and school would benefit from a new broom. Lots of old pupils there and all said when they were pupils he was the new broom.

Choir practice so diabolical surely everything had to be alright next week. Unless, of course, it's true six people are on holiday and Pat's husband has finally banned her from the choir for ever. Must go round and see her.

July 18 Saturday

Dennis arrived at 9am with gear for Youth Group's end of season Games Day. I'd forgotten to ask Sam to move sheep so Dennis and I penned them up in a corner and cleared their deposits from grass. Laid out fun golf course, tennis court, cricket pitch, rounders square and athletics track for welly chucking and slow bicycle race. Colin suggested croquet on front lawn and Dennis agreed – hadn't realised croquet takes about two and a half hours if you play as ruthlessly as Colin does.

Colin managed to persuade them to have a go and not engage in duels with the mallets and we'd been playing an hour, with the kids obviously plotting a quick sprint home, when a distressed parishioner called him away. We decamped to fun golf – anyone taking over five minutes a round disqualified. Played all other games and presented the 'cup' (coffee mug with footballer on it) to winner. Colin so disappointed Judith and I played croquet with him. Judith won. Didn't like to mention promised evening out.

July 19 Sunday

Dennis took Eucharist. Wish congregation hadn't congratulated him quite so warmly or repeated quite so often that Colin could now 'go off on holiday whenever you feel like it.'

July 20 Monday

First of three sessions to choose new head for school. Wasn't told how it went.

Joyce's publicity for next week beginning to appear. Colin said at 6pm why didn't we go out for birthday dinner. Because Judith had gone out with Hank ten minutes earlier, not having been told she was needed to sit, I said. No problem, he said, he'd ring round the congregation to get a volunteer. Naturally the first he tried said she'd be delighted. Eleven tries is my average and once I had to have a relay of people who could only manage an hour each.

Went into town to The Fiddlers to avoid being recognised. Two people from village greeted Colin with varying degrees of emotional and theological troubles before we had time to study the menu, one woman who'd met Colin while he was visiting someone else in hospital asked if she could come and see him some time with a problem, and the waitress, explaining she'd overheard people addressing him as Vicar, poured out a diatribe against her own Vicar (Johnson). I had the duck and fruit salad and Colin the steak and Black Forest gateaux.

Colin pressed tip into hand of waitress and she handed him a scruffy note, which we read in car. I said to pass it to Geoffrey the Rural Dean as Johnson can't actually refuse to marry parishioners unless they're divorced. Colin said that was the coward's way out.

Waitress's Note

Please I want a proper wedding in Church and would be glad if you could oblige. Me and Mike have been together a year but no – you know. He's living with his mother. The reverend here says I can't because of Glenda but I don't think that's fair, do you? I fell for Glenda when I was 16 at a leaving party at school with a boy, I can't remember who. My mum said to get rid of it but I don't think that's right so I left and come here. Glenda is a good girl and Mike says it's alright. We can be a family. That Vicar says to come to Church at his but his breath smelt and I feel awkward not usually going. I go to school carol services and sometimes watch Songs of Praise. If you can help I could come of a Sunday morning some time. Thank you for reading this.

July 21 Tuesday

Colin rang Johnson about waitress. Didn't say result. Helen from S School rang to say we're almost full for tomorrow with children and parents. Wasn't that great? 'Great,' I said. Realised ten minutes after she rang off tomorrow's the Sunday School outing to seaside. I'm going with Anne and John. Found old note to myself saying SS outing 22 July, outside pub at 10am, take packed lunches, leave something for Colin.

Judith strangely subdued. She can't not want to be on holiday surely.

July 22 Wednesday

Anne and John enjoyed outing. I didn't. Helen put me in charge of three small children. Sam locked himself in ladies' loo. Cleaning lady scrambled over from next cubicle to rescue him. By that time Jilly and Lisa (ultra clean kid) had vanished – last seen by passer by heading for pier. Sam and I raced up and down pier peering overside. Public announcement that they were in an office looking for Sunday School lady in the pink dress (would have said it was blue myself but decided to claim them). All four of us spent hour on various rides until I was giddy, Jilly was sick, Sam and Lisa hungry. Settled down to doze on beach as they asked for donkey rides. Told them to wait a bit and play on sand. Woke up as attendant told me: 'Don't worry. They've not gone far. They're stuck.' All three had set off to meet the tide and were stuck fast in mud, crying. Refused to let them move beyond coach stop until it was time to go. Parents blamed me for all incidents, especially Mrs Turner.

Helen said four of play's main characters for Saturday afternoon are on holiday, could I get Youth Group to read in parts. Recorder player also away so could I take over. Practised this evening – awful.

July 23 Thursday

Most of day practising recorder. Not much better. Stanley rang to ask if I'd arranged transport for trestles and chairs from hall or tents for Saturday in our garden. Or removal of sheep or opening of hall in case of rain. Hadn't done any of that.

Sam refused to move any furniture even before I asked over the phone, but did move sheep. Leonard moved ducks. Joyce out so no ideas from her about removals. Desperate. Stanley rang to say only joking, he'd got it all arranged.

Judith requisitioned kitchen to cook bits for tomorrow's disco. Went to final rehearsal of play. Now almost unrecognisable as mine but much jollier. Some of Youth Group reading in – quite good. My recorder playing put everyone off. Costumes wonderful, especially donkey. Christopher wouldn't take off donkey outfit, insisted on going home in it. Joyce rang to say I wasn't to worry about support for Derek's organ recital tomorrow. She'd managed to collect 'quite a little coterie' of friends and colleagues for it. Just as well. Colin and I the only other people I know of going to it.

July 24 Friday

Dennis rang to say should he bring Youth Group round to get fete things ready. They had a great time making bunting out of old material and setting up daft games. Tamar said her brother would bring his old van for competition to guess how many people could fit into it. Two boys volunteered to be guinea pigs and have wet sponges thrown at them. Two tents arrived and owners put them up. Left corner of garden free for the play. I set out tea party for teddies which my Teddy Wellington is expecting to entertain tomorrow.

Organ recital interesting. Very interesting. Derek played selection from Bach, Handel etc. like man discovering a foreign country – cautiously. Then selection from The Beatles and Les Miserables very fast as though expecting a thunderbolt to fall on him. Colin and I with dozen or so from congregation plus Joyce's cronies clapped enthusiastically. Colin said a few words. Joyce wearing a beautifully tailored pale blue suit and what I can only describe as a coiffure. Derek joined her and her friends and they all went off together. Miss Cavendish said she'd helped her choose the suit. I said it was an improvement on her usual brown and Miss Cavendish said she didn't think we'd see any more brown.

July 25 Saturday

Fete rained off – teddies saved the day. Hoards of people (all ages) turned up with hoards of teddies (all ages) when skies opened. Judith said the hall was ready for disco so I shouted: 'In the house' and we transferred sideshows and people indoors. When I finally got in (soaked) there were games and raffles in all rooms, St John Ambulance team demonstrating mouth to mouth resuscitation in the hallway, six people in the kitchen doing teas (too flustered to notice greasy oven?) and teddies up the stairs. Judith and Wellington judged entrants – oldest, best loved, tattiest, etc. Decided to do play in Church tomorrow. Raised £480. Everyone said it was much more fun than usual.

Anne said disco was 'brill' except for big girls drooling over the DJ and John being there with friends. John said it was 'alright, especially Judith and Hank.' Judith slammed through the house at 11pm and shut her door. I woke John up to ask what he meant by 'especially Judith and Hank.' 'They shouted,' he mumbled. 'Hank said she should be a nun.'

July 26 Sunday

Judith red eyed at breakfast. Hank had wanted her to go to a party. She said she'd got to clear up after disco. Hank said if she was so damned religious she'd better leave him so that he could play the field. Then he left – noisily. I tut tutted sympathetically for three minutes before inquiring anxiously about how much the disco raised. £70. Very good.

Play in Church terrific. Someone's mother baked real rolls for feeding of 5000 – all eaten before we started. No miracles forthcoming so cast had to mime eating. Donkey costume looked as though it had been slept in (I think it had). One child knocked over elaborate flower arrangement, some disciples trampled blooms underfoot and two others fell over on wet floor – made crowd scenes more effective.

July 27 Monday

Judith moping about so she and I took children to a bird garden. Colin toiled in vegetable patch all day, stung into action by comments on Saturday.

Note From Judith To Hank

Please find enclosed one silver plated necklet, three rings and unreliable watch. Please feel free to recycle them to any irreligious female you have the good fortune to meet. I hope she enjoys the experience of being shouted at in a public place. Goodbye – it was not worth knowing you.
PS You're a shit.

July 28 Tuesday

Judith packed and departed before we got up leaving note on kitchen table about spending time with friends and being back for beginning of term.

Colin gave up on veg patch, decided on burnt earth policy. Sprinkled everything in patch with paraffin, set light to it. Called me to see really good bonfire. Flames rather close to borrowed tent still up on lawn, I thought. Wind altered direction. No time to take down tent so we got inside it, tore out pegs and ran through paddock holding up tent with only our feet showing underneath. Collapsed under it in paddock. Emerged to see Barry the fireman there – always dashes to scene of great swathes of smoke. He helped us damp down fire, gave lecture on bonfires. Stanley came at end of it all and said: 'That garden looks like the day after the Somme.' Would be quite funny if it wasn't true.

July 29 Wednesday

Sam brought back sheep and Leonard ducks with ribald comments on garden. Leonard offered a deal – he'll take over the veg patch and keep the produce, tossing us the odd onion or so.

Jill Medlicot rang to say she'd be round tomorrow for Vicar's Letter for magazine and any bits from organisations we wanted in. I set up excuses for what I knew would be Colin's late delivery of said Letter. She said she'd had so much material perhaps it would be better if he only put in a Letter every two months. Colin speechless with indignation. His Letter written, typed and in envelope for collection by 4pm. Just getting in bed when I remembered I hadn't written anything myself. Typed it out straight away. She's the sort that arrives very early in the morning.

July 30 Thursday

Jill on doorstep at 8.30am – on a school holiday morning! 'He managed to finish it then,' she said cheerfully. 'Blackmail usually works.' Anne and John already up watching TV. I didn't know there was TV at that hour. Too late at 9am to go back to bed so made a disturbed day even worse by cleaning the oven.

July 31 Friday

Dennis rang to say organisers of town's carnival short of floats and had asked our Youth Group to enter. Not to panic. He'd had some ideas and members keen. Perhaps I could help a bit. Carnival August 22, after our holiday, so agreed. They're doing a Mad Hatter's Tea Party. I suggested asking sewing ladies to help with costumes. Brilliant idea, he said. They'd already agreed. (This parish begins to run itself. Perhaps we ought to quit while we're ahead and go to Mike's inner London parish. Told Colin and he said 'Who's ahead? Hundreds hardly know where the Church is, kids never darken the doors, Women's Group sowing dissension, bossy women taking over choir and magazine etc. etc.')

August 1 Saturday

Woke at 3am worrying about not having seen Pat at Church since 12 July. Had her husband really banned her from coming? Would she take any notice? Ought I to interfere in husband and wife altercation? Yes, if wife is one of few sopranos able to reach top A. Asked Colin if he'd rather do the interfering and he said he thought I'd do it better. Went round, found Pat alone, and the answers are yes, he's banned her and yes, she's agreed. He's up for a major promotion in an American company based over here and she's a vital accessory at all social gatherings, usually on Fridays, and on Sundays they play golf with the bosses. 'Sorry' she said. 'Perhaps when he's selected . . .?' I said. 'Perhaps,' she said mournfully.

Went round to Joyce's three times during day to ask how she'd deal with playground bullies wanting to butter up bosses. Out. It's school holidays for goodness sake.

August 2 Sunday

Waitress Janice at Church with her little girl, Glenda. Left before I'd changed from choir clothes. (Most people do leave pretty sharpish. It's like having a fire alarm go off every week as soon as the choir leaves for the vestry). Colin surprisingly bolshie over Johnson this time. 'I've told her to stay with someone in our parish for a while to get a local address and I'll marry them and tell Johnson when the deed's done. That man ought to be made to leave.' He also said it was a pity I didn't manage to speak to Janice and welcome her. Lots of people, he said, left without seeing me and someone asked him why his wife never went to Church.

Very stressful to be blamed for not doing something you do do – I must mention it at clergy wives.

August 3 Monday

Perhaps I won't have to mention it. Elsie Bailey's solved the problem of mass stampede – serve coffee so they stay behind. 'We used to have sherry on festivals,' she added hopefully. I think we'll stick with just the coffee for the time being. I told Colin and was going to suggest having a rota of coffee servers when he said: 'Good. Don't forget the biscuits. There's a socket at the back for boiling the kettle.' No rota then. Just me.

CHAPTER ELEVEN

HIGH FINANCE

August 4 Tuesday

Day started badly and got horrendous. Terrible smell in the garden first thing. Colin inspected the drains. He was covered in filth with his arm down the hole when Arthur puffed up the drive to collect him for the dreaded Quinquennial Inspection of the Church. Surveyor waiting impatiently. (So that's what Q on calendar meant. How could Colin not know? How many appointments does he make with people or situations beginning with Q?)

He arrived at Church an hour late – still slightly smelly despite bath – to hear surveyor mention the dreaded phrases 'death watch beetle' – 'roof repairs' – 'estimated £30,000.' Stanley, Arthur and Colin shut in sitting room all afternoon – ten cups of tea each. Stunned silence every time I went in, except once they were discussing how much of the work they could expect Fred Padget to do when he was fully recovered again.

Half an hour after they left Padget's son, visiting from Australia, rang to say his father would be suing the Church for his fall.

1am Colin remembered he'd left manhole cover up. Stumbled out, dropped watch down drain.

August 5 Wednesday

Colin said he told emergency meeting of PCC called to discuss the problem that it was 'an opportunity for out-reach into the community – an exciting chance to show how central we were to the life of the village.' They had responded well, he thought. They all seemed keen on getting started. Fund raising would start when everyone got back from holiday – but he wondered if he ought to cancel ours and stay behind to 'work out a stragetgy.' 'A strategy for getting a divorce and running the damn place on your own you mean,' I said. (Ever since I heard of that stress workshop I keep acting stressed – why is that?)

I think the holiday's safe. He seemed to be trying to ask me something but never got round to it.

Extract From PCC Minutes

The secretary having read the draft report of the surveyor at the Quinquennial Review, the Vicar addressed the meeting on the subject. Mr Bessant stated that he thought what was needed was not 'airy fairy' platitudes but a practical plan of campaign. Raising such a sum as £30,000 would require firm leadership and discipline. It was proposed by Arthur Penfold and seconded by Stanley Wilson that an appeal be launched and a committee of the PCC be set up to formulate fund raising projects, such committee having the power to co opt. There being no volunteers for membership the meeting was adjourned.

August 6 Thursday

Colin round at Padgets' to placate son about Fred's injury and try tactfully to ask when he would be ready to do small jobs for us and could Mrs Padget join the fund raising committee. Son eventually said it was alright this time but his dad was not to do any more work for us – ever. The question of Mrs P never came up. Actually jumble sales are probably not the answer to raising £30,000 I said later to Colin, and wished I hadn't. He said nothing. Just sighed.

August 7 Friday

So that's what Colin's been meaning to ask me – can Janice the waitress and Glenda stay here for a few weeks so she can be married in our Church? Well yes if Judith doesn't come back early and claim her room back. He blurted it out over breakfast and I worried what Anne and John would think. Anne: 'Can I be bridesmaid? – everyone else I know has been one' (answer 'no' as lack of money, fear of reprisals from Johnson will make it too quiet for such fripperies). John: 'But she's got a girl. Can't I go and live in a tent in Luke's garden when she comes?' (Answer: I'll ask his mum if John can stay over with a tent for one night when we get back from holiday).

Shopping to collect up clothes, first aid kit, teabags and any other food children, and Colin, will be unable to do without in a foreign land. Hurtled into town for foreign money, found ferry tickets and other essential bumph after four hours' hard searching. Took gerbil round to Doris at Post Office. She was surprised – I forgot to ask her to mind him – but willing. Got up in early hours to search for passports – in drawer with electric plugs, screw drivers and drawing pins. Colin came down after half an hour, fully dressed and about to drive to hospital in town to see elderly man (Maurice Sproggett).

August 8 Saturday

False alarm. Mr Sproggett sitting up in bed demanding jam sandwiches and why was the Vicar hovering about him 'like a bloody old vulture.' Colin left quickly to get car checked at garage.

Everyone markedly unenthusiastic about holiday – John why couldn't he take his bicycle on car roof as he'd often ridden on right hand side in the village so that would be alright; Anne: why couldn't she stay behind with friends as sitting in a boat all day and having absolutely no one to talk to would be so boring; Colin: why couldn't he take six enormous theological volumes to catch up on his reading when we stopped in a quiet canal overnight and the children were in bed? 'Told you it would be boring,' said Anne. 'I'm not going to bed ever,' said John.

Remembered ten minutes after shops closed I hadn't got enough biscuits, coffee or plastic cups for Church tomorrow. Spent evening scrounging them from people.

August 9 Sunday

'Thought you'd gone,' everyone said, 'Why couldn't Dennis do the service?' It seems he's so popular they're willing to overlook his dry sermons. Coffee and biscuits went down rather well, except with those who wanted tea. Everyone stayed so long the Sunday School erupted in before they'd gone. Forgot to talk to Janice and Glenda about them coming to us. Forgot to ask anyone to do coffee next week – perhaps someone will volunteer. Am writing this just before leaving and will then leave it behind. See you next week diary.

August 16 Sunday

That was it then, the Great Family Holiday. Rather good really once we found the right canal and the right boat, which was not the beautiful private cruiser we tried to get into but the scruffy crate beside it. All crossness and moaning vanished from Tuesday to Friday (sight of cases being re-packed and thought of inevitable note from Arthur brought it all back). My dream of blissfully sitting in the sun reading as we drifted through idyllic scenery unrealistic as one expensive meal out forced me back into the galley for the rest of the time. At least I could admire idyllic scenery while peeling potatoes. Also too many locks. Can't swim so in deathly fear of falling in to my death every time we moored until John pointed out he was a very good swimmer so he did it – and fell in, but with no ill effects. Anne made a friend of a girl from Birmingham on a boat that followed us throughout. Quite sorry to have to leave the boat – even the galley – for the last time. We may even come back next year.

When we got back I saw Arthur's note on the mat but hid it until morning.

Postcard From John To Gran And Grandad

This is a picture on our canal but not our boat. I helped at the locks because mum is scarred and I am not scarred. Mum said not to say I fell in but it was alrite.

August 17 Monday

Arthur's note said Dennis and Elsie had to rush off to visit grandchild in hospital as soon as we'd gone – same grandchild as before but this time real appendicitis. No service in Church last week. Most of congregation went to Methodist service – it starts half hour later so they had time to consider the theological implications: would they have to sing modern choruses and would they get home in time to get the Sunday dinner? (Same things I'd have worried about). Mr Sproggett died in hospital. His family ferocious that Colin was not there when he was needed – after all that's his job, isn't it? Don't bother with funeral, they told Arthur. It's a cremation and the funeral directors have arranged a 'very nice Vicar' to do the service, called Johnson! (Arthur's exclamation as he knows Johnson from the interregnum when he turned up drunk to Evensong and made a pass at Pat in the choir, which she didn't dare tell her husband about for fear of murderous repercussions).

Heard later Dennis's grandchild had had the operation and was doing well. Tried not to worry about whether Dennis would be back in time to organise the YG carnival float. No good. I'm very worried.

August 18 Tuesday

Youth Group boys on doorstep first thing (9am) to say when could they start work on carnival float. Dennis had said they could go to Sam's to decorate a lorry he'd lent them. (How did Dennis do that? Colin lets Sam get away with murder and sheep in the garden and I'm sure he couldn't borrow a wheelbarrow). Also, would I go with them? I was about to murmur an excuse about looking after my children when Anne's friend came to pick her up to go out somewhere with her family and John negotiated permission from the boys to go along with us.

Took rest of day cleaning up lorry. Mad Hatter's Tea Party too silly, they're coming as Star Wars. Girls turned up when we'd finished. Boys agreed to include a Carnival Queen and court if they kept out of the way until the float was finished. (Wonder if film makers mind us taking liberties with their material and what about costumes?) Sam agreed to the boys working on their own if I can't get there.

Janice and Glenda arriving tomorrow.

August 19 Wednesday

Janice and Glenda took four journeys to bring round luggage and all day to unpack – using both spare rooms. Was I sure I didn't mind? Colin had suggested it as Glenda always had to have lots of space for her bits and pieces. I saw the point. She's acquired more bits and pieces in her eight years than Judith had in her 30. 'I feel I owe it to her,' Janice said, unloading Glenda's three new dresses, a CD player still in its box and 32 videos. There have been several other boyfriends in Janice's life apparently, not all of them as willing as the latest to accept Glenda into their lives. Glenda's also acquired insights into grown up behaviour I'm not sure Anne and John are ready for. 'Granny says perhaps now mummy will stop sleeping around,' I overheard her telling them confidentially. 'I told her mummy doesn't. She always sleeps in our house. What's it like having only one daddy?'

August 20 Thursday

Janice may or may not sleep around but she certainly sleeps in. She got home from work at 12.30am (I thought the restaurant closed at 10.30pm) and was not up at 10am. Had to take all three children with me to carnival float. John and Anne helped a lot, Glenda sulked until girls arrived and said she could be in their court. It's amazing what heavy duty tin foil, odd bits of wood, polystyrene and tough cardboard boxes can do to a lorry, even if it doesn't look anything like Star Wars. Janice overjoyed when I told her about Glenda's starring role and practically any one of her dresses, apart from school uniform, would do for a carnival princess. Told Colin that and he said not to be judgmental as Janice was only trying to do the best for her child in a difficult situation. Janice out until 1am.

August 21 Friday

Dennis back. Grandchild recovering well. Much impressed with carnival float but not sure it was Star Wars. They all agreed and now it's the Court of King Arthur. Which knight was going to wear the outer space outfit? I inquired, sarcastically it has to be said. 'It's amazing what skilled needlewomen can do,' he said.

August 22 Saturday

Didn't feel at all 'I told you so' (honestly) when kids turned up at Sam's farm and found the float lorry gone – knights' court bits and bobs on barn floor with a note from Sam: 'Need lorry for bailing. Back soon.' Carnival to start at 2pm. We all waited, girls too. Lorry back at noon. We put it together hastily. Too late for judging but we joined back of procession. Glenda sat with Tamar on a rather wobbly castle and when it rained all the cardboard swords and helmets disintegrated. All agreed it was worth the effort. Invited to take part in carnivals on next three Saturdays. Sorry, need the lorry Sam said. 'I'll think of something,' Dennis said and they all went off quite satisfied. Wish I had that sort of faith.

August 23 Sunday

Methodists returned our lot's visit. How embarrassing as many of us on holiday, including most of the choir, and they have an instrumental group and a youth choir. Their minister's moved and a new one's expected who's great on United Witness. 'Happy clappy they mean,' said the Miss Wallaces in unison. 'Organs are for Church. Violins and flutes are not natural,' said Mrs Fearns. Colin explained that the organ was the newcomer, but I could tell he was uneasy about this chumminess. I pointed out that if we joined forces sometimes he would have fewer sermons to write.

August 24 Monday

Woken at 8am by almighty crash. Colin, Anne, John, Glenda and I rushed into drive in night clothes. (No sign of Janice). Builders unloading scaffolding. About to renew house roof – employed by Diocese, they said. We had been informed – true, up to a point. We were told it was to happen, but not when exactly. 'How long?' we asked. 'Three weeks – roughly,' one of the men said. 'I should pull your curtains, love.' Janice! I rushed up to her room to tell her to beware builders – no sign of her. Builders set to work. Janice home at 10am – stayed over with friends to avoid disturbing us in the early hours.

August 25 Tuesday

Builders so loud and messy I took three children out to various parks and amusements all day.

August 26 Wednesday

Finding a carnival float is taxing even Dennis. Suddenly every farm vehicle in a ten mile radius is urgently needed. Rang Joyce in desperation – Derek answered. Discussing music for

Michaelmas he said. Michaelmas? Colin's never yet managed to convince anyone here of the existence of angels, let alone of the need to give them a festival. Joyce too busy to come to the phone but sent message later to try milk depot.

August 27 Thursday

Sorted – milk depot will lend lorry if we put sponsorship notice on it. We agreed, but the idea of sponsorship reminded me. When were we to start raising £30,000 for quinquennial repairs? Suggested sponsored something to Colin. 'Don't mention repairs,' he said. That's because a huge crack has appeared in most of the upstairs ceilings, the builders smashed two windows, dropped tiles off the roof narrowly missing two parishioners and left today saying they'd got another job but would be back ASP (their abbreviation). Rang Diocese to complain. 'They're the lowest tender,' said the Diocesan Secretary's secretary. 'Not when you've repaired the damage and paid compensation to the injured,' I said.

August 28 Friday

No sign of builders but Mike, Janice's intended, turned up for marriage preparation talk with Colin at 3pm. Janice out with friends from work. Mike in building trade, rude about firm we've got, inspected roof from scaffolding and drew in breath. Janice arrived 5pm with two friends, slightly merry. Colin said secretly to me he was worried about whether she was 'mature enough' to be getting married. Glenda's mature enough for herself and her mother I told him. What she doesn't know about 'relationships' is hardly worth putting in a soap opera. Then he got Glenda to join the three of them and things seemed to go better after that. I hope so because Mike's a nice bloke and a good builder; Janice is not too bad, just flighty; Judith will want her room back; and how dreadful if Johnson proved right not to marry them.

August 29 Saturday

Carnival Float did really well – second in Youth Class.

Beginning to wonder about Judith. When is she coming back? If she needs her room will it be easier to persuade Janice and Mike to live together for a couple of weeks or get Janice to confine her belongings to one spare room. 'Mummy and Mike want to save themselves until they're married,' Glenda said when she overheard me put this moral dilemma to Colin.

August 30 Sunday

Youth Group's carnival triumph mentioned in notices. Three of older people in congregation said what Youth Group was that? Had it got anything to do with the Church? Janice's banns read. Miss Burnett from old people's bungalow said over coffee why did our older daughter have a different surname from ours – had I been married before? Tried to explain about Janice living at the Vicarage temporarily, and no relation of ours but she lost the plot before I'd finished outlining Johnson's idiosyncrasies.

Noticed a gaggle of people, mainly youngish, around Colin. Helen, Sunday School teacher and twentyish was holding forth – usually she's tongue tied with adults, fine with under tens. Later he said they'd 'ambushed' him about having 'informal' Family Services once a month. Colin's sure it's the Methodist influence – for informal read non-Eucharistic. 'My' Helen (I recruited her three years ago and I think she's a great find) wants a group to organise a friendly little service with choruses, child instrumentalists, simple prayers. It could be good, I thought, but I didn't say so. They want it, they can persuade Colin, the Miss Wallaces, Miss Burnett etc. 'What does Joyce say?' I did ask. 'Nothing. She left very quickly,' said Colin. 'What about Derek – can he cope with choruses? Does he mind strange instruments?' 'Didn't ask him, he'd gone.' The people involved say they'll come round in the week to discuss it.

August 31 Monday

No builders but a postcard from Judith from Australia. Anne cried all day. I shed the odd tear and even John's lip trembled suspiciously. Colin hoped she'd make the right decision about marrying Hank – but dubious marriages are what's on his mind these days.

Bumped into Stephanie in the street and casually mentioned the postcard. She chugged off on a new moped in great spirits mumbling something about Church calls. Personally I now think Colin would have even more doubts about her and Bernard.

Postcard From Judith

Dear all of you,

As you can see from the postmark I'm rather too far away to be back by beginning of term. Hank & I can't live with each other or do without each other. Decided to try what pastures new will do for relationship – Sidney about as new as we could find. We're settled in a flat, hoping to get jobs, even get married. Thanks for coming to my rescue when I needed somewhere to stay. Perhaps I'll see you again some day. Thanks again, look after yourselves

CHAPTER TWELVE

CLOSE HARMONY

September 1 Tuesday

Kitted out the Church porch for tramps again after Scouse Mick –
one with pinching shoes and too small anorak – mentioned it had
lost its blankets and sleeping bag and been severely trashed. 'I
expect it was Irish Ted,' he said. 'I'd heard he was on one of his
benders – you just keep them kids of yours out of his way when
he's like that.' (Another thing no one mentioned when Colin was
at college, this catering for streams of tramps, some drunk. Must
be why I'm not good at it – never take enough time to talk to
them about their life stories). Made Mick the usual sandwiches,
filled his flask and took him up to the bathroom as Colin asked
me to on his way out on visits. Why a bath? Colin says Mick's
going for a room and wants to make a good impression. With a
room he can get a job and face his sister again. That sounded
hopeful, I said. 'Oh, he won't really go for it, he never does.
Anything permanent frightens him to death.' Anne and John
unmoved by sight of strange man coming out of bathroom, just
asked to share the sandwiches. Glenda just said: 'I expect he left
home after a broken relationship.' Gave Mick a lift to town for his
next port of call – the Vicarage where they do his laundry.

September 2 Wednesday

Asked John who he wants to come to his birthday party Friday.
Doesn't want a party – 'treats' all the rage now. Sounds
expensive. Tried to push party idea. 'Why do we always have to
be different?' he said. He must be getting old if he's noticed that.

Family Service deputation came – Helen, Pamela Wilson,
Jill Medlicott (magazine editor) and four others from Mothers and
Toddlers and Stephanie. Colin so pleased M & T getting involved
he agreed. Second Sundays. Colin will try to push objectors
towards 8am Holy Communion. He's still uneasy.

September 3 Thursday

Solved the birthday problem. Decided to take John and three friends to seaside. Playing on beach doesn't cost anything so should get away with a few ice creams and my birthday cake. Anne to go to a friend's. Colin nearly asked Glenda to be one of three – I threatened him with resignation from everything if he even mentioned it to her. We'll lie to her about the whole thing.

September 4 Friday

John fairly pleased with second hand bike we gave him considering the hints at much more expensive things that have gone on for weeks. Delighted with day at seaside as it poured down all the time and he and friends had to spend the afternoon in a games arcade. 'Ace,' he said. 'Expensive,' said Colin – but only secretly afterwards to me. Janice cross at having to look after Glenda all day.

Jill Medlicott turned up to choir practice with two choruses they want for Family Service – gave them to me and vanished. I handed them out and waited for explosion – all looked at Joyce. Derek said he was in a hurry and could we start. Played Shine Jesus Shine and we sung it, followed by Give Me Oil In My Lamp. Looked at Joyce again 'And we'll just practice hymn 234 for this Sunday. You know the rest,' she said. We've never 'known the rest' enough for her before, but, oh well, I'd had a tiring day.

September 5 Saturday

Bernard rang to say he's only too pleased to lend us his overhead projector for Second Sunday as they seldom use it now they've moved on to multi-media approach. I didn't tell Colin.

Builders came, took down scaffolding and went away. I suppose I should be glad the Diocesan Office took notice of my complaint but I'd like to be sure they've got someone to finish it and repair the others' damage.

September 6 Sunday

Children moody – ours and everybody else's. 'That's the trouble with long holidays – it gets them out of the school habit,' one mum said to me. School! Yes, you've guessed it diary. I forgot. Usual scramble. 'At least we haven't got Old Doddery,' said John. Good heavens a new head. Forgot that as well.

Family Service gang asked me to be sure to bring plenty of squash and biscuits next week for the family friendly service. 'What are we now. Family unfriendly?' said Mrs Fearns when she overheard that. Oh dear. Dennis told them he'd work out some involvement for the Youth Group in future months. Organisers far from overjoyed. Obviously 'friendly' is limited to the cute little ones.

Janice's banns passed in merciful silence. Two weeks to go.

September 7 Monday

Colin's opinion of new head teacher. 'Wonderful – an excellent choice. Now we're getting somewhere.' John: 'She says there'll be more Church.' And Anne: 'Everyone says it's our fault because dad helped choose her.' She started the term with a full Church service instead of informal prayers – three hymns, prayers of thanks for the holidays and help in schoolwork etc. Colin preached and told The Parable Of The Child Who Forgot To Learn (his parable not Jesus's) (Did the child Jesus have a literacy hour and if so how did He do I wonder?) 'It's only the first day' I say. 'Everyone has to try new things on the first day.'

'You shouldn't undermine what she's doing,' Colin said later. I told him he didn't know what it was like being Vicarage children as his father was a bank manager.

Rang Diocesan Office about builders. That firm's gone out of business. We're about the 92nd in queue of jobs for new firm, when they find one for what they're paying.

September 8 Tuesday

School gets worse – or better, depending on your viewpoint. Mrs Croxley's infiltrating religion into the school's everyday life and there's a service once a week and even rumours that Halloween has been outlawed – no spending half the term making masks and witches' outfits for a party. 'Can't we go to where Sophie Leighton-Syme goes?' asked Anne. 'Her parents pay and we can't afford it and anyway it's a Church foundation and the kids practically live in the Chapel,' I said. I think Anne despairs of finding an oasis of secularism in her world.

Elsie rang to ask if I'd pick her up tomorrow around 9.30am and I know she heard me furiously trying to remember what it was and trying not to exclaim in horror when I realised it was the Clergy Spouses' Stress Day.

September 9 Wednesday

Mega stressful day for all. 15 minutes into talk by Lay Reader doctor on Managing The Moment (stop screaming at kids, husband, parishioners and builders for a second to take stock) and phone went for Penny from two parishes along. Their pet dog run over by parishioner's car. Husband comforting parishioner, wanted someone to comfort children. She left. Johnson's wife weeping throughout a semi jolly talk on Managing Ministers given by a bachelor Priest with a degree in psychology, who was the only one there not to know Johnson.

David, spouse of female cleric, absent. We spent half afternoon speculating on rumours about him and female Sunday School Superintendent. My main reason for stress – forgot to take packed lunch. Everyone had to give me an item of their's.

'Honestly, what do you think of today?' Sally Jeffries asked as I left. 'Very . . . thought provoking,' I said. 'It was a complete disaster. It just shows how useless I am at organising things,' she said. Elsie stayed behind to comfort her – good thing as any comment I made would be bound to come out flippant.

Family stressed out as meal wasn't ready on time.

September 10 Thursday

When will I ever learn? Asked Colin what was happening over raising £30,000 for Church repairs. 'Nothing,' he sighed. 'Everyone's waiting for everyone else to start so nothing can happen – unless you?' Hmmmmm 'And I suppose we ought to do something about the Harvest supper,' he added. Double hmmmmm.

September 11 Friday

Choir practised Family Service music. Mutterings, mainly from altos as it's all unison. Three of the older children came along to practice instrumental accompaniment – one flute, one violin, one recorder. All beginners. We looked to Joyce for suitable response. 'We'll just run through the Evensong psalm,' she said. 'I must get on.' Stephanie and Bernard arrived with overhead projector and we left her taking instructions in its use.

September 12 Saturday

New Youth Group session. Four new kids came to 'see what it's like.' All went to Sam's barn to dismantle carnival float. 'Great,' said huge lad with shaved head (Jake?) Yes, but how to follow that. 'I thought we'd do some cooking,' said Dennis. He's losing his touch, I thought and it must have showed on my face because he said: 'They'll jeer at first and play the fool but they'll come round, believe me.' 'Perhaps they'd like to cook the Harvest Supper,' I said sarcastically. Never be sarcastic with either of the Baileys, diary. 'All of it would be too much, but I'll suggest we do the first course,' said Dennis.

September 13 Sunday

Now that's what I call upstaging. The first Family Service – overhead projector to illustrate talk by a lay person also featuring puppets, enthusiastic clapping, instrumental group (marginally better than on Friday) Women's Hour group storming out midway. Colin asking people to 'pass the peace' – and what will we always remember about it? Joyce and Derek announcing their engagement!

Miss Cavendish looked smug as the only one in on the secret. Everyone else stunned. Shouldn't have been, of course. Both have been acting strangely for weeks.

'We're not losing an organist but gaining a musical partnership, I hope,' said Colin into the stunned silence. 'We'll live in Derek's house after the wedding – for the time being,' said

Joyce. 'They'll leave and then what will we do for music?' Colin said to me gloomily. 'There's the instrumentalists' I said.

Janice, in Church to hear banns, the only person to mention Family Service. 'Not what I thought Church would be like,' she said sternly. 'I want proper hymns at my wedding, with a proper choir.'

Help! – how to recruit a choir for a person no one knows at a week's notice and with Joyce incapable of focussed thought. 'I thought she'd told you about the choir,' was Colin's helpful comment. 'Surely you can find someone.' Rang round, got four possibles. Janice wants 'traditional' so we'll dig out Lead Me Lord from our wedding repertoire (only anthem in our wedding repertoire as it happens) (Double Help! – Joyce and Derek will need something gold plated for their wedding ceremony and will Derek double as organist and bridegroom?)

September 14 Monday

Bessant rang to say he 'assumed we required use of the hall for the Harvest festivities on Monday week – together with all the appurtenances' (assume he meant cutlery and crockery). Leonard rang to say his brother willing to give the entertainment if I had not thought of any other bugger. (Knew from his voice he knew I'd forgotten the entertainment and that I knew he knew). Had to agree as last time I forgot and we had auction of harvest produce lasting two and a half hours.

Another school service. Colin suddenly noticed it means lots of extra sermons. Talks of getting 'lay involvement.' 'Not mum,' said Anne firmly. 'I'll lose the few friends I've got.'

September 15 Tuesday

You know, diary, my feelings on dogs: dirty, smelly, dangerous waste of space and money; and children's: cuddly, fun, friendly, worth every minute and penny. Well, we seem to have acquired one. Briefly, I hope.

Parishioner dumped a Collie looking mongrel with John while I was hanging out the washing. 'He said he knew we'd look after him, being a Christian family,' said John. 'I think he's that man that sits at the back in Church. He brought a lead so I'll take him for a walk.' I rang everyone I could think of and all said it sounded like Roger Mottram – Church the regulation three times a year (Christmas, Easter, Harvest). Dog apparently beats up other dogs and barks a lot. Neighbours threatening to shoot it. Colin wrested it from John to take back to Mottram – came back with it. He's looking after a sick wife, walking the dog too much of a commitment. Affectionate pet, loves children, sure we'll give it a good home. Name's Muffin. 'Please mum,' said John.

It's just a trial, diary, honestly. Glenda's frightened of it, stays in her room. 'She'll get used to him,' said Colin. 'But she's only here until Saturday, the wedding day.' I said. He forgot (?) to tell me – Glenda's staying with us while her mother's on honeymoon in Tenerife for ten days. 'Has anyone remembered to tell Glenda?' I asked a trifle sharply. 'I think her mother's waiting for the right moment,' he said.

Letter From Joyce To Her Friend Hazel

Dear Hazel,

I feel I must admit to being a little hurt by your reception of news of my approaching nuptials. The 'relationship' between your brother and I you so forcefully mention was purely that of friends, consisting mainly of a shared interest in what I now recognise as a rather limited range of early music. My own tastes have been considerably widened by the influence of my fiance, as I hope your brother's may be in the fortunate event of his meeting a true soul mate – as indeed I feel I have. You are both welcome to attend our wedding in the Parish Church where this harmony of interests has flourished, although I feel I should point out that the service may not meet with your exacting standards and, in any case, the journey may prove an inconvenient one.

You mention my brother as being likely to share your doubts about the advisability of the step I am about to take and his welfare being endangered by the union between Derek and myself. However, he sees the situation as a chance for a new, independent lifestyle and has left to backpack across Africa on his motorcycle.

With kindest regards to yourself and your brother, Joyce.

September 16 Wednesday

Muffin the dog woke us up at 6am, barking and rushing about. John got up and took it for a walk.

Archdeacon rang to ask what progress on quinquennial work. Colin said about to start on minor work before major fund raising begins. News to me and I should think everyone else in parish.

Colin met Arthur and Stanley in Church to think of something to start quickly (dreadfully efficient the Archdeacon and likely to check up). I hastily called meeting for tomorrow evening to launch fund raising. Will shoot first person who says 'coffee morning with raffle.'

September 17 Thursday

John still ready to take Muffin for early walks. Discovered another of dog's bad habits – keeps rolling in unidentifiable, horrible stuff and getting smelly. No amount of washing removes whiff for hours. Might be handy getting rid of unwanted visitors, but we don't get many of those.

Had a sneak preview of Janice's wedding dress – warned Colin of possible embarrassment over very low cut bodice. Reception organised by Janice's workmates at club in town. Bit awkward, she said, can't really have Glenda there or any friends from the village. In other words, we're child sitting from Friday (hen night) to whenever they're back from honeymoon. Glenda now sulking about: dog; missing reception; missing honeymoon. Think she's got a point on all of them and she's not even tried on the bridesmaid's dress yet.

Local firm started work in Church taking up few rotting floorboards.

Fund raising meeting: Dennis and Elsie, Mrs Wilson, Mrs Fearns, Steve and Jill Medlicott, Helen. Agreed to: sponsored parachute jump (Steve has experience, will teach others); sponsored swim involving school; pet show (my idea, I've got dogs on the brain); hymnathon; Firework Party. Mega drama on history of Church and village would be nice if someone? wrote it, directed it and sold tickets (I left room to get coffee – mistake as they've minuted that I volunteered to do it). Not agreed: jumble sales, Flower Festival (preserve of parishes with Vicar's wife who can arrange flowers).

September 18 Friday

Workmen removing floorboards found a skeleton. Arthur and Stanley argued over what to do – stop work, report it, discover who it is (Arthur); rebury it, say nothing (Stanley); don't know (Colin). Archdeacon seen driving up. Bury it was Colin's casting vote. Archdeacon not altogether impressed with progress as floorboards replaced very inexpertly.

September 19 Saturday

3am woken by Janice's friends decanting her from car into our drive after hen night and her staggering upstairs and waking Glenda for a maudlin interlude about becoming one 'big happy family' and how they both 'loved her to bits.' Glenda at 8am saying she's not going to wedding. 9am negotiated trip to cinema with her in return for her attending. Agreed. 10am got her into bridesmaid's dress on promise of party with friends at McDonalds. 10.30am Glenda in full regalia woke Janice. Arthur rang and said he'd put white ribbons round hole in Church floor to make it less unsightly for wedding photos.

Wedding went off fairly OK. Glenda cried and turned her back in photos. Stephanie in the choir cried as Bernard has just announced his engagement to childhood sweetheart. I was so harassed I told her to subscribe to the Additional Curate's Society. Derek jazzed up the Wedding March. Joyce giggled. But, Janice only 15 minutes late, only four drunken guests and two hangovers. Bridegroom must have been there but can't say I noticed. Muffin trotted up aisle mid anthem smelling badly, closely followed by John with broken lead. Colin assisted both to leave.

Glenda subdued but tearless by evening. Told me she regards this as her 'real' home.

September 20 Sunday

Had to ask Glenda to go to Church as couldn't leave her alone. She said she regarded it as her lifestyle now.

Mrs Padgett gave Colin a note. Stanley said where were the Harvest Supper tickets. 'I don't believe in limiting it,' I said with dignity. 'Everyone's welcome.' Not really alarmed as we always get about 50 people whether I remember the tickets or not.

Just as we left Miss Williams said 'I see you've lifted some floorboards. Did you find a skeleton?' I mumbled something and left.

Note From Mrs Padgett

Just to say Vicar I'm off down the Methodists. I expect they'll appreciate a person's years and years of organising jumble sales. Use your talents you're always saying in the pulpit but now there's parachuting and fireworks and sponsored this and sponsored that, a jumble sale's not good enough. I noticed no one mentioned the hundreds and hundreds we've raised for the Church with jumble. I only hope you won't be disappointed in these new ideas. My son thinks me and his father are mad to keep working for the church. You can be just as good Christians sitting at home, he says.

September 21 Monday

'I can't think what you've got against jumble sales,' Colin said to me. 'They make some money and everyone enjoys them.' Reminded him the last time he went to one was three years ago – he always has an excuse for dodging them. But I agreed to ask Mrs P to organise one for the appeal – with a raffle.

Glenda to school, no problem except the usual one of the vast amount of luggage she seems to want to take from huge felt tips sets to designer trainers.

Question of skeleton still niggling me. Tentatively asked Doris at Post Office if she knew anything about it. A mistake that. It's probably her great great grandfather who fell to his death while painting the Chancel ceiling and was buried there out of respect. She hoped he'd be reburied 'properly.' Colin quite tetchy

113

about me interfering – we'll have to hold a ceremony and invite Doris's family while keeping it quiet from everyone else, the newspapers and the Archdeacon. Told Doris we'd see to it. 'Until you mentioned it, I'd forgotten all about it,' she said.

Mrs Padgett rescued from nonconformity at the price of a Jumble Sale as she's relented. I offered to help at said event and even give raffle prize.

CHAPTER THIRTEEN

THEM DRY BONES

September 22 Tuesday

Moaning session with Elsie Bailey about continuous run of jumble sales, harvest suppers, parachute jumps and visiting tramps. Also unpaid secretarial work such as answering phones, covering up Colin's forgetfulness and generally being a peculiar species known as Vicar's Wife. Bet Vicar's husbands don't get landed. 'What you need,' said Elsie, 'is a job now the children are older.' Hmmmm. Last time I was in paid employment I was a glorified copy taker for a newspaper. Could I cope with workplace politics, regular hours, taking orders?

September 23 Wednesday

Colin asked by Diocesan big wigs to give lay adults evening classes in basic theology, from next week. Someone else has dropped out. All I have to do is provide coffee and biscuits and help with paper work. If I had a job I'd be too busy to do any of that.

Stephanie arrived – in a car – to cover story of skeleton dug up and discarded to distress of family. No more moped. No more forgetting stories embarrassing to Church. She's abandoning men in favour of a career, preferably on a scurrilous tabloid. Also were we practising harvest anthems on Friday because if so she'd have to find cover for a council meeting. Asked myself whether I had anything to do with her being such a strange, mixed up creature.

Colin phoned her later to say we would re inter the skeleton in small private service with surviving family, when we'd established who he was. He was cross the story would eclipse the launch of our appeal in the public consciousness.

September 24 Thursday

Local paper day. Recruitment pages full of jobs too skilled, too boring, too everything for me but wrote for forms for two of them anyway. No word to other three – sufficient unto the day are the arguments thereof, especially about regularity of meals and ferrying to friends, clubs etc.

Scoured music cupboard for harvest anthem. All Victorian, pre combine harvesters. Joyce and Derek arrived to discuss date for wedding. Not to worry, she said. Derek inspired by the turn of romantic events and has written his own anthem about fruitfulness. Colin and I exchanged glances of tortured laughter suppression and accepted their word it was probably the most exciting new work for harvest since the Victorian heyday. Also simple enough to learn at one practice? I asked. A choirmaster knows his singers, Joyce pointed out.

School harvest service. Children did play about child exploitation in Third World and *Anne was in it* (she kept that very quiet).

September 25 Friday

Actually anthem's quite jolly – cross between Joyce's madrigals and Derek's show tunes. An improvement on modern hymns that manage to bring in tinned foods and space travel. Choir a bit sniffy, but also a bit overcome by the romance of it all. Mrs Fearns summed it up for all of us – Mr F never wrote any music on her account, not even a thing about fruitfulness that's replaced the good old anthems. I told them to be ready to give a reprise at Harvest Supper in case Leonard's brother's jokes are too few or too blue and we had to bulk out the entertainment.

September 26 Saturday

Helped Sunday School arrange vegetables in Church – safest place for me when decoration's going on everyone thinks. Remembered, just in time to avoid the Easter disaster, that Mrs Clampet does the porch now and Mrs Bessant her window. Mrs Clampet ready with several ornamental marrows, quite happy.

Youth Group made a few quite good quiches. Won't tell supper guests that members began the evening taking each other's bikes to bits and switched to kneading pastry rather too soon for hygiene purists.

116

September 27 Sunday

Good houses. Anthem OK with everyone except two or three farmers, who only come once a year and expect an action replay each time. (What do they think Church used for during rest of year – a glorified hall? General stores? Someone's barn?) Produce sold at end for good causes except what we need for supper. Several people mumbled about 'making something for the supper' – there always seems to be enough.

September 28 Monday

Never mind the Youth Group's dirty hands, it was me that nearly poisoned the parish. Made stuffed marrows from left over produce in Church, only it was gourds I picked up by mistake. They taste so horrible you couldn't eat them even if starving in the desert for a fortnight. Stampede to loos where all spat it out. Anne, John, Glenda and rest of children and Colin, who think vegetables are yuk, managed to escape. Also baked potatoes nearly raw. Half cooked them at home, put in hall oven, fused all the lights. 'I informed all hall users of the need to rewire the hall when funds are available and meanwhile to refrain from using the cooker.' Bessant said after he'd got the lights on again. He didn't say anything to me about it, honestly, diary.

Leonard's brother ate some gourd and potato and his language fruitier than the fruit salad. Jokes ditto. So I wheeled on choir to sing anthem and two hymns. 'I shouldn't apply for work in a restaurant,' Elsie whispered to me. I did penance by doing all the washing up.

September 29 Tuesday

Glenda finally gone – miss her (only a bit). Janice and husband arrived after school to take her, two days after getting back from honeymoon. 'We thought it would be nice just to have some quiet time together,' said Janice. Wouldn't it just, I thought. Glenda wept buckets at leaving Muffin, first dislike forgotten. 'We've bonded,' she said and then 'Mum can I have a dog?' I opened my mouth to offer Muffin's services as pet, but the look on John's face was too much for me.

September 30 Wednesday

Received job application forms in post – one of them cook in hospital. I burnt it. Filled in Building Society receptionist and left it hidden to fester.

October 1 Thursday

Three people asked when I was going to announce launch of Roof Fund. Sent off application for receptionist's job – told family. John asked if there was time to take Muffin for a walk before tea; Anne said could she have her ears pierced; Colin said when had I thought would be a good time for Roof Fund launch.

Ears pierced? Where did that come from? I said no and looked to Colin for support. He left, mumbling about 'visiting.'

October 2 Friday

Helen dropped in music for three choruses for Family Service next weekend. Mutterings from nearly everyone about silly words, dafter actions (clapping and swaying) and all unison. Colin put his head in to inspect progress on floorboards (none) and got set upon by everyone. Promised to put in one ordinary hymn. Still mutterings.

Anne rather quiet over ear piercing except to say everyone at school had theirs pierced.

October 3 Saturday

They're obviously desperate at Building Society – got an interview date for job (Tuesday 4pm, don't forget diary).

Suddenly out of blue those missionary people wrote (Ellery, mysterious missionary from parish). Did we still want lights? If so they are willing to come over for a service of dedication to meet local representative about raising their profile in our village – perhaps a link with one of their people abroad. Several of them in need of prayers and cash. (Now, not a time to ask PCC for either, because of roof, but Colin said suggest a service and 'take it from there.')

'I may be working when you want the arrangements made,' I said. 'If we made it November Family Service there would be new people in,' he said. I wrote back suggesting they come in a week or so to make arrangements.

October 4 Sunday

All coming round to ours tomorrow to organise launch. Hymns the most boring A & M to balance next week. New school head in Church. She's really Bernard's parishioner but he's 'too lax'. 'Wonderful,' said Anne. 'Church in school, school in Church.' 'Just wait until she experiences Family Service,' I said. 'There's lax for you.' Anne and Colin managed grim smiles.

October 5 Monday

Launch to go with a bang – literally. Firework party 16 October in our garden weeks away from Village Guy Fawkes (but only yards away from our house). Barry the fireman volunteered by his wife to supervise. Alright, but I think I'll stay in and do baked potatoes (properly cooked this time) as I know from previous experience with Sunday School and Youth Group that many children are terrified of even the smallest sparkler. It'll be free, to soften people up for a year of fund raising – Arthur's brilliant idea. Short service first in Church with Archdeacon asked to do the honours.

October 6 Tuesday

Interview went very badly. They discovered I'm good for nothing but making tea at Mothers and Toddlers or making a fool of myself at Youth Group – neither skill wanted at Building Society but they'll let me know. Colin almost said something when I mentioned interview at home and Anne said: 'Shall we be able to afford for me to have my ears pierced if you get a job?' I explained it was mutilation of body not money behind refusal. 'I'll tell Zelda about mutilation,' she said smugly. 'Her mother's taking her to have hers done tomorrow and you said her mother was a find for the Church and could help with lots of things.' She is and I did. Oh dear.

October 7 Wednesday

Told Doris at Post Office about Missionary Service just by way of conversation (she noticed address on letter and asked, as she does). She said if we could make all this fuss about some old guy who nobody really remembered when were we going to hold a special service for her relative everyone knew about and who had been heartlessly disturbed in his grave.

'Any more extra services and it'll be like a supermarket for special offers,' quipped Colin. (Do other professional households have their 'in' jokes as well as jargon? If so are the doctors', dentists', undertakers' quips any funnier?)

October 8 Thursday

Skeleton service to be next Tuesday. Doris thrilled, going to contact every relative. Also thrilled she's leaving the Post Office to work as receptionist at Building Society. Congratulated her. Haven't told anyone yet that I'm doomed to Vicarage duties for ever. That sounds dramatic, but I shall have to be dramatic to grab a second or two of attention.

October 9 Friday

It's official. Choir on strike. Colin forgot to put in ordinary hymn among choruses for Sunday. 'Where will you draw the picket line?' I quipped. No one laughed but one alto said 'My cousin goes to Mr Johnson's Church. It's very traditional. She says they desperately need choir people.' I sheepishly mentioned service for skeleton and would the strike still be on. Fortunately one member, a second cousin by marriage to the skeleton's grandson, and she recruited one or two volunteers for Tuesday as a special concession. The strike is bound to be over by next week, isn't it? Colin said very likely if I restrained myself from joking.

Stephanie showed a healthy interest in strike and skeleton – I had to be glad she's so thoroughly recovered from Bernard and, it seems, even Colin.

Joyce and Derek away Sunday morning visiting even more relatives.

October 10 Saturday

Dennis in plaster from right fingers to shoulder – fell over a mound of members at Youth Group. Six weeks immobilised at least Elsie told me. 'I have to admit I've never really appreciated all he does,' said Colin. 'We'll have our work cut out to cover for him.' It's alright for him as he's just got an 8am Communion to do extra most weeks. I'll have Youth Group. 'You may have to shelve that job idea,' he added. So he had been listening! Had to own up I hadn't got it anyway.

October 11 Monday

Choir stalls empty this morning. Three members came, plus me, and sat in congregation, clapping and swaying with best of them.

'Good idea, Vicar, having just instruments. They make a change from the organ and choir. Perhaps we'll go in for more when Derek and his young lady leave,' said someone. 'It's always good to take a fresh look at what we're doing,' said Colin. Traitor!

He felt sorry in the evening though as there was no choir at all at Evensong, just me and I sat in the congregation. Derek there but Joyce still visiting, he said. I feigned ignorance of how to sing the psalms as my contribution to solidarity and the whole thing broke down at verse six. Colin hastily sat down and signalled to the Bible reader to start. I meant not to join in the hymns but Colin had, again traitorishly, put in favourites of mine so I couldn't resist joining in.

October 12 Monday

Scouse Mick called on his way to a hostel somewhere. 'No luck with the room then?' I said. 'They made it too hot,' he said. 'It can't do anyone any good living in that heat.' 'But winter's coming on,' I said, prolonging our conversation much beyond the usual. 'Anywhere inside has to be better than outside.' 'Oh, I'll definitely have something before Winter,' he said. 'I'll not be on the road this winter. Any chance of me staying in the Church porch tonight?'

Dennis sent note round (left handwriting) about Youth Group. Some of it must be his idea of a joke, mustn't it? Just for that I'll get Dennis to organise and attend make up do – I never use the stuff.

Asked Anne to bring John home from school tomorrow afternoon, start getting tea ready as I shall be at skeleton service. No reply just 'Zelda has promised me three pairs of her earrings when my ears are pieced.' Alright , I give up. After all, I expect John the Baptist was just the type to have had pierced ears, nose and naval. Anne agreed to after school tasks.

Made cakes for after service tea. There will only be about a dozen at it, won't there? Colin said he hoped for more as he'd found out a lot about the skeleton man and wouldn't want it to fall on empty pews.

Dennis's Note

The bad news is – I'm in plaster for six weeks, not driving for at least 12. Medics want me to rest as well owing to my extreme old age. Good news is, plenty of ideas for Youth Group sessions – from members themselves. Don't panic- they realise some of them will need me to come back to help.
Make robot with old bicycles, ex-computers, car spares etc. Enter TV's Robot Wars with it.
Take part in dirt track racing.
Repair TVs and video machines.
(Girls idea) Have visit and demonstration from make up artist.

October 13 Tuesday

Your owner is now a proper career woman, diary, not an adjunct to a Vicar and mere mum. Building Society wrote – able to offer job. Rang Doris to make sure it's alright. 'Fine' she said. 'The money's even worse than the Post Office and the hours are longer.'

Made some more cakes – could be my last if the Building Society hours are that bad. Haven't told Colin or kids.

About 60 people arrived for skeleton service in Church – some family, lots of villagers, faithful choir members, and Retainer from Big House sent by Mrs Delaware. Stephanie and two other reporters and assorted photographers. Colin said few sentences and prayer – then fire broke out in porch. Likely a tramp left a cigarette end there too close to blankets. Steady flow of curses from Leonard expecting he'd have to clear up. Barry the fireman, distant relative of skeleton, present and had just quenched flames when Archdeacon arrived to inspect the repair works. Colin, when I asked him, whispered he thought he'd managed to stall the Archdeacon as there's not much work to show, but obviously he hadn't. Also two people from mission society arrived to talk to 'Church officials' about Ellery memorial.

Finally angry woman arrived with Muffin, followed by John, followed by Anne, followed by teacher. Muffin had escaped from house, roamed streets, frightened the woman's child and run to school to find John. Both John and Anne left without permission. Reporters spoilt for choice about which story to cover. Mayhem until Colin shouted over the grave: 'Let us pray.' Silence, except for Leonard cursing over do gooders who let tramps use consecrated building.

At end Colin invited all round to Vicarage for 'cup of tea and a biscuit.' I alarmed Archdeacon by inviting him to firework launch of appeal. If this afternoon is what we can do at a simple service, it hardly bears thinking about what we can do let loose on fireworks, I could feel him thinking. Got rid of Ellery couple by promising to give out collection boxes and install lights 'soon.' Angry woman over tea and cake admitted her child might have teased Muffin.

'On the whole I think it was a good occasion, pastorally speaking,' Colin said as he dropped off to sleep. 'There's nothing like a disaster to unite people.' Perhaps Scouse Mick could arrange a small fire more often – in the interests of pastoral outreach – I commented to his sleeping back.
Must write and accept job;
Must tell family about job;
Must call choir together to sort out Family Service strike business;

Must arrange dirt track visit and robot making for Youth Group;
Suppose I'd better find someone safe to pierce Anne's ears;

Sorry diary – shan't have time to speak to you for a while.